"I'd like to kiss you,
but I just washed my hair."

Bette Davis
Cabin in the Cotton, 1932

GW00684686

Gift Aid Re...

20 **70904163** 9999

Vintage Hairstyling

Retro Styles with Step-by-Step Techniques

Second Edition

Lauren Rennells

HRST Books

Cover Design, Illustrations, and Design by Benjamin Rennells
Photography and Design by Lauren Rennells unless otherwise noted

Published by HRST Books
Post Office Box 18429
Denver, Colorado 80218-8429 U.S.A.
info@vintagehairstyling.com; www.vintagehairstyling.com

Copyright © 2009 by Lauren Rennells. All rights reserved. None of this book,
in part or in its entirety, may be reproduced without the written permission
of the author.

Library of Congress Cataloging-in-Publication Data
Rennells, Lauren.
 Vintage Hairstyling: Retro Styles with Step-by-Step Techniques / by Lauren
Rennells
100 p. 26 cm.
Includes bibliography.
ISBN-13: 978-0-9816639-1-3
1. Hairdressing. 2. Hairstyles. I. Title.

Library of Congress Control Number: 2009931475

Printed in the United States of America

Thank you

Many wonderful people helped make this book possible. First on the list of thank you's goes to my parents for guiding me and standing with me on my journey, my brother Ben for being my design consultant and art director, my brother Todd for proofing my elementary grammar, my many teachers of beauty along my path including Miss Lil and Miss Cindy, Dena Olivett, Davida Simon, Leslie Snyder, and Jenece Amella and thank you to my friends for being my cheerleaders through this process.

Thank you to all of the very beautiful models that sat for the book including Katherine, Melinda, Kris, Cheryl, Grace, Sara, Jo, Alix, Akira, Marlyn, Alyssa, Julie, Valerie, Mandy, Marianne, Amanda, Devon, Katelyn, Aly, Pam, Chanda, Kailee, Miranda, Lily, Jenece, Kyleigh, Lindsey, and Vivian. Your lovely faces make this book.

Table of Contents

Notice to Readers

The reader is encouraged to take all safety precautions in performing any techniques or activities herein. By following the instructions the reader or anyone acting on behalf of the reader willingly assumes all risks of harm in connection with performing these techniques. The author and HRST Books are not liable or responsible to any person or entity with respect to any loss or damage caused, or alleged to have been caused, directly or indirectly, by the information contained in this book.

Introduction

There was something very special and beautiful about women in the early- to mid-20th century. The way they dressed was elegant and the way they wore their hair was feminine. Hanging on my mother's wall is one of my favorite photographs of my grandmother, in the 1940s, with cascades of curls all around her face and down her shoulders. How were these complicated hairstyles created? What is a girl to do in the 21st century when she has not been trained from birth on how to set and brush a pin curl?

This book will shed light on the process and serve as a resource for hairstyles for many occasions, and will assist someone who wishes to create her own style. Some styles in this book are done traditionally, starting with wet pin curls, drying, and then combing out. Others are modern versions using today's tools and techniques. I encourage you to study the entire book. It is full of useful information that can be applied to many different situations.

After mastering some of the techniques, look for other images and try to figure out what combination of techniques were used to create a style. What size of pin curls were used? What is the starting length of the hair? How can you fake that style or get the same effect with a different hair length or texture? It may be an exact re-creation, or a modern version that has the same feel.

Watching movies adds dimension to the hairstyles. The style is clearer when seen from every angle as an actress moves across the screen. Use your DVD-player's pause button to pause the movie at different intervals and use your point-and-shoot digital camera with the flash turned off to capture the angles for reference later. Your computer's screen capture capabilities are also useful for this.

There are many other resources for finding images for reference. Check your local library, your parents' and grandparents' homes, web image searches, on-line auctions, and antique stores for books about Hollywood photographers; photographs; movies; and other material. Old yearbooks carry close-up, clear photos in portrait form. One of my favorite reference books is a 1948 University of Houston yearbook I picked up for $15.

The Internet is absolutely the greatest resource. The website www.imdb.com, The Internet Movie Database, has information and numerous photographs of all the famous film actresses of the past, many of whom are mentioned in this book, and information on their movies.

No matter what your goal is in reading this book, I hope, above all else, that you will learn. Identifying vintage styles and piecing together how to complete them was a labor of love for me. With a little luck, I will have saved you the same trouble.

To Start

Some hair tools and products have remained essentially the same through the ages. Bronze razors, tweezers, hair curlers, mirrors with ivory handles, and wooden combs have been found dating from 2000 B.C. or earlier. Ancient Egyptians used hairpins made of bone and wood. Although the materials may have changed over the years, these tools and products were all designed for the same purpose: styling hair.

Many of these solutions developed from other technologies. Women figured out they could move the hose attachment on a vacuum cleaner from the front of the machine to the back and the air would blow out instead, creating the first hair dryers. This technique was then combined with electric heaters. Early handheld dryers were not powerful enough to dry hair and were more often used to blow hair away after cutting. In the 1950s, a plastic dryer for home use was developed and made available in many pastel colors chosen to coordinate with a lady's boudoir.

Different forms of what we know as hairsprays have been around for thousands of years. We refer to them as sprays because we are familiar with them in spray form, but most ancient cultures had mixtures used to make the hair stay in place. The aerosol process was patented in the 1940s and was based on wartime insecticides. This helped the hairspray industry grow.

The tools and products laid out in this section are today's tools. Some are new designs and some designs have not changed much in thousands of years, but they are all available brand-new today. Refer to the resources section for places to find them.

Hair Products

Thermal Sprays protect hair from damage when using heated appliances like curling irons. If using a curling iron often or on a high heat setting, thermal sprays are important. They also help hold the curl longer when using hot rollers and curling irons.

Hairspray holds the finished hairstyle in place and helps control hair during styling. Light hold hairspray makes hair more pliable for brushing out dried wet sets.

Setting/Shaping Lotion is a must when doing a wet style like finger waves or pin curls. It makes the hair more pliable for forming and helps the hair hold its shape while drying.

Pomade/Hair Dressings were in use through the entire early twentieth century. They come in different consistencies for different effects. They are often used like a gel for hold. For ladies' styles they add shine, control curls, and direct hair. A hair dressing with a consistency close to vaseline is the most useful in women's styles.

Water is the most forgotten styling product. Throughout this book there are examples of wet hair sets that would not be possible without it. It helps create a stronger, longer hold that will withstand forming and shaping and lasts for days.

Wet Set Prep: If choosing a style from the book that is a wet set, be sure to get the hair wet throughout. Although it does not need to be dripping wet, if the entire shaft is not wet, it will not hold after it dries. After the hair is wet, work a shaping lotion through the entire head to make the hair more pliable.

Pomade Use: Pomade has been used on every hairstyle in this book. It helps keep the shape and controls the hair. When working with a dried style, get a very small amount of pomade on fingers and work it through your hands. As you are working with the hair, continue to get pomade on fingers for more control.

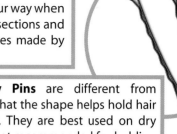

Duckbill Clips are useful for keeping hair out of your way when working on different sections and also help control waves made by pin curls.

Double Prong Clips are used to hold large pin curls in place when hairpins do not have enough strength. Use the kind with a gap at the hinge for fewer kinks in the hair after it dries. These also help hold barrel type rollers like velcro rollers.

Bob/Bobby Pins are different from hairpins in that the shape helps hold hair very tightly. They are best used on dry styles and not recommended for holding wet pin curls. They create kinks in wet hair that will not always come out after the hair dries.

Hair Fastening Tools

Single Prong Clips are handy for pinning up curls from a curling iron. After a curl is formed, pin it against the head to cool for a much longer lasting curl.

Hairpins provide a looser hold that is perfect for wet set pin curls. For thicker hair a few may need to be used but the open prong keeps kinks at a minimum. They are not generally strong enough for holding up dry styles compared to bobby pins

Hair Combs, not to be confused with styling combs, are used for holding back large sections of hair in finished styles. Because the handle of the comb shows, they are great for decorating.

Barrettes come in many different sizes depending on how much hair needs to be held back. If too big, they don't hold. If too small, not enough hair will fit. They can be decorated with flowers or bows for added fun.

Banana Clips spread the hair wider than a ponytail holder or a barrette. Decorate it with flowers and put it on horizontally at the base of the neck.

A **Styling Brush** has strong bristles for control. Use it to brush out pin curls that may need some work to loosen up and hang nicely. Its wide shape is great for brushing out styles, but can be too wide for brushing out waves.

The **Rattail Comb** is most useful for controlling curl sizes. Use the rattail end to section out hair for pin curls or hot rollers. The closely placed teeth are perfect for ribboning hair to get all the strands straight before curling. The teeth are also useful for teasing hair for fullness.

Hair Styling Tools

A **Styling Comb** often has two sections with different amounts of teeth. The side with more teeth is designed for greater tension which is helpful when combing out a style. If you find that there is so much tension you can not get the comb through the hair or it pulls too much, flip it to the side with fewer teeth for more ease.

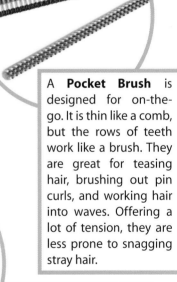

A **Pocket Brush** is designed for on-the-go. It is thin like a comb, but the rows of teeth work like a brush. They are great for teasing hair, brushing out pin curls, and working hair into waves. Offering a lot of tension, they are less prone to snagging stray hair.

Thin Teasing Brushes are designed for back brushing, which is teasing with a brush. They offer all the tension of a brush for brushing out a style. But, because they are thin, they are easier to maneuver around the head and snag stray hairs less.

Specialty Styling Combs are also available. They offer various uses from styling tight styles, combing out curl fluff with ease, teasing, or lifting at the base of the hair shaft. When looking through the step-by-step images make note of which comb is being used, but keep in mind that they can be interchangeable.

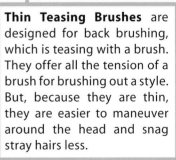

Velcro Rollers use Velcro technology to hold the hair against the roller. Hair "sticks" to the roller so no clips or pins are needed to keep it from slipping off. Designed to be used on both wet or dry hair they create the longest lasting curl when used on a wet set. Double prong clips may help when used on longer hair.

Hot Rollers come in many different sizes. Most sets of rollers will have metal prongs used to hold. Special clips are also made to fit around the roller to hold it in place and offer less chance of slipping. Not all rollers are equal. When you buy a set let them heat for 15 minutes. If they are not so hot they are hard to touch, then take them back.

Hair Curling Tools

Soft Rollers take the place of harder rollers when you may need to sleep while hair dries. They are more comfortable but the hair can take longer to dry on these as air does not circulate around them as well.

Steam Rollers/Setters combine both heat and water in the form of steam to create a longer lasting curl. The strength of the curl is not quite as good as a wet set but generally has more staying power than a hot roller curl.

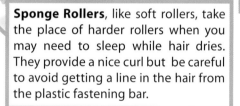

Sponge Rollers, like soft rollers, take the place of harder rollers when you may need to sleep while hair dries. They provide a nice curl but be careful to avoid getting a line in the hair from the plastic fastening bar.

The **Hooded Hair Dryer** speeds up drying time on wet sets. There are many models for home use that fold up nicely. Many are now offering ion technology that helps dissipate water molecules for quicker drying time. If hair is not wrapped too thick in a roller or pin curl, hair can dry within 30-60 minutes on a high setting. Note that many bonnet-style dryers will not fit over large rollers.

The **Curling Iron** is by far the quickest, easiest way to get a long lasting curl. Although it does not last as long as a wet set curl, if done properly and allowed to cool while pinned to the head, the style will have lasting power. They come in sizes from 3/8 of-an-inch up to 2 inches. A 1/2 inch or 3/4 inch curling iron was used for the curling iron styles in this book. Make sure you are using a thermal spray to protect hair from heat damage.

The Silhouette

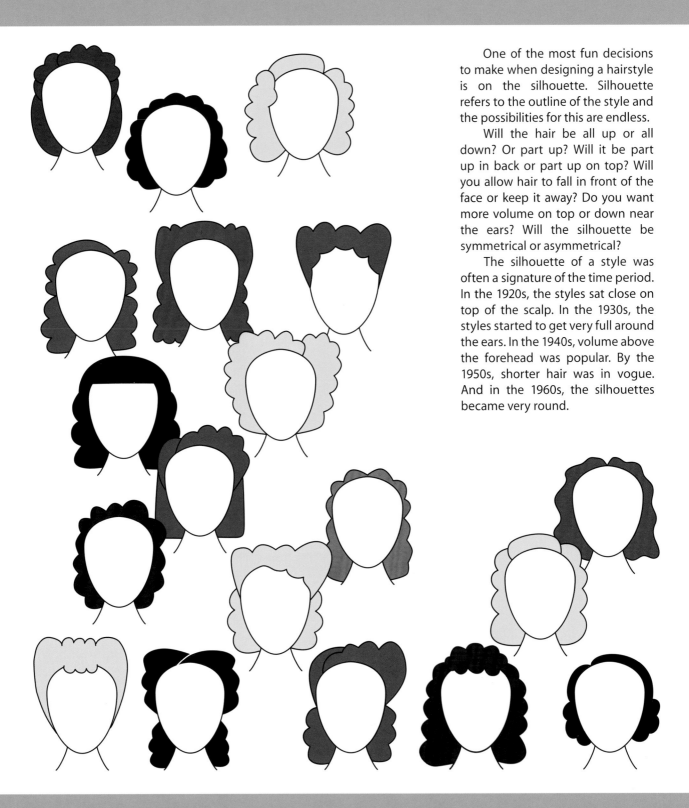

One of the most fun decisions to make when designing a hairstyle is on the silhouette. Silhouette refers to the outline of the style and the possibilities for this are endless.

Will the hair be all up or all down? Or part up? Will it be part up in back or part up on top? Will you allow hair to fall in front of the face or keep it away? Do you want more volume on top or down near the ears? Will the silhouette be symmetrical or asymmetrical?

The silhouette of a style was often a signature of the time period. In the 1920s, the styles sat close on top of the scalp. In the 1930s, the styles started to get very full around the ears. In the 1940s, volume above the forehead was popular. By the 1950s, shorter hair was in vogue. And in the 1960s, the silhouettes became very round.

If you are searching the many resources out there for ideas on styles to try, note the hundreds of silhouette variations you see. Most of the time, there will be an accompanying year to give you an idea if it is the same time period you are trying for.

When deciding on which silhouette to use the most important considerations are hair length and texture. If hair length is too long for a style, you can always pin it up for the same feel.

Texture refers to the thickness of hair. There are techniques like teasing and back-brushing for adding fullness to fine hair. But keep in mind that hair texture has a great effect on how a style looks in the end.

Do not feel bound to trying for one look because the hair appears to be the same texture and length as what you are working with. Try it anyway if you like the way it looks. With a little creativity the same feel is possible.

✦ The Curl ✦

One thing that all hairstyles had in common was the curl. Webster's New World Dictionary defines curl as "1. To twist (esp. hair) into ringlets 2. To cause to bend around". Some curls may be small and buoyant. (Think Shirley Temple.) Some curls may only be at the ends of the hair, like Greta Garbo's. Some could be better described as a bend, as in a chignon. But they are all curls. Only the degree of the curl and placement makes the style different.

The manner of creating a curl has not changed much, although the products and tools have definitely become safer and more sanitary. Special muds were used to set curls in ancient Greece. A curling iron called a calamistrum was used in the Roman Empire. Curling irons have been found in ancient Egyptian tombs. Through the ages irons have been heated over gas stoves, flames, or hot ashes.

The development of the long-lasting curl has been a goal of many inventors. A web image search for "Nessler perm machine" will bring you to a hair styling tool created in 1905 by Charles Nessler. A woman's hair was wrapped around a chandelier-like machine of large metal rollers. An electric current was supplied to the rollers to heat them in an attempt to make the curl last longer. It didn't have great results and the hair often broke in the process. The machine has a brief cameo in the movie *Red-Headed Woman* starring Jean Harlow.

In 1932, chemists Ralph L. Evans and Everett G. McDonough developed the first mass-marketed machineless permanent wave. And in 1941, a method was developed that used waving lotion and was referred to as a cold wave. This wave replaced virtually every permanent waving method and is still used today.

In this section, you will find descriptions of the methods used throughout the book to create curls. From the most basic hot roller set to the many considerations in creating a pin curl, this section is important in understanding the differences in creation and effect.

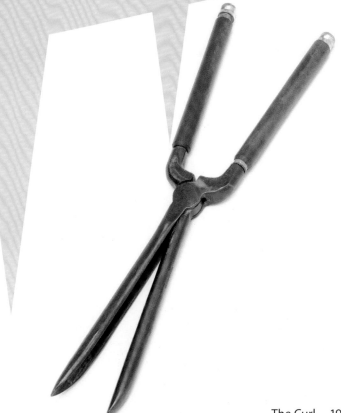

✦ Curling with Heat ✦

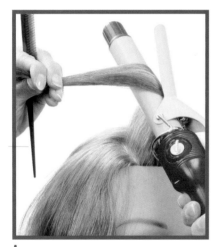

Pin the curl up to allow it to cool for staying power.

Curling Iron

It is important to remember that hair is at its strongest the closer it gets to the scalp and it can be very fragile at the ends. For this reason, when starting a curl, start it at mid-shaft.

1. Insert the hair and let it wrap around part way before closing down the shell.

2 and **3.** Keeping hold of the end of the hair at first for control, begin rotating the iron and releasing the tension periodically, allowing the hair to work around.

4. To protect the scalp, insert a comb between the curling iron and the scalp.

5. Extreme heat over time will damage hair, so be sure to use a thermal styling product before. Do not start a curl at the ends of the hair. The hair is fragile at this point.

1

2

3

4

5

Base Direction

Base Direction refers to the direction the hair is pulled before the curl is formed. For the purposes of this book, curling iron base directions will be referred to as a **Volume Curl**, **Off-Base Curl**, or **Length Curl**.

1. For a **Volume Curl**, start the curl at a 45° angle away from the direction the curl will go.

2. As you roll the hair into the iron, you will notice that the finishing point lands on top of the base of the curl. It is referred to as a **Volume Curl** because it creates the most volume.

3. For an **Off-Base Curl**, the hair is held at a 45° angle towards the direction the curl will go.

4. As you roll the hair into the iron, you will notice that the finishing point lands "off" of the base of the curl. This curl is used when no fullness at the scalp is desired.

5. For a **Length Curl**, the hair is held at an even lower angle. And the curling iron is not rolled all the way up to the scalp.

6. In the finished curl, the hair that is 2" from the scalp is left out of the iron. The effect, when it is brushed out, is curly ends with added length. This curl is also used to mimic the uncurled crown area of many styles of the 30s, 40s, and 50s.

1

2

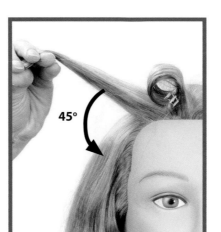

3

4

5

6

Hot Rollers

1. To get the best effect from a hot roller, the base of the piece of hair rolled into the roller should be the same width and length as the roller you are using.

2. Spray a thermal spray on the hair to get the longest lasting style.

3, 4, and **5.** Roll the hair from the ends to the scalp. If having trouble getting the ends in, hold the tail of a rattail comb flat over the ends while getting the roll started.

1

2

3

4

5

Basic Roller Set

6 and **7.** Many of the hairstyles in this book started with a basic roller set. This just refers to using medium or large rollers, either rolling back or down. The set seen here will have the effect of creating volume and bend in the hair. Hot rollers are not best for creating small tight curls.

6

7

Base Direction

As with a curling iron, **Base Direction** refers to the direction the hair is pulled before rolling.

1. Hair for an **On-Base Curl** is held at a 45° angle away from the direction the hair will be rolled.

2. Hair for a **Half On-Base Curl** is held straight up from the head.

3. Hair for an **Off-Base Curl** or **Length Curl** is held at a 45° angle towards the same direction the hair will be rolled.

4. This illustrates the differences between the different base directions when hot rollers are used. The roller to the right is an **On-Base Curl** and the roller sits directly on top of the base of the hair. The middle roller is a **Half On-Base Curl** with only half of the roller sitting on top of the base of the hair. And the curl on the left is an **Off-Base Curl**.

5. The **On-Base Curl** creates the most volume and the **Off-Base Curl** creates no volume.

Whether curling iron, hot rollers, or wet set rollers are used, the same effect is achieved in volume control with these base directions.

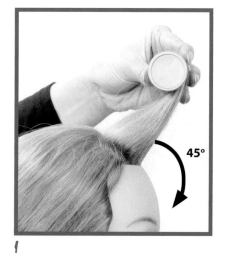

1

2

3

4

5

The most commonly used method for curling during the early and mid-twentieth century was water, often after a perm. Whatever shape hair has been formed into while wet, it will keep that shape after it dries. This form of curl lasts longer than heat but not as long as a perm. A **Wet Set**, as it is referred to in this book, will last for days if taken care of and protected.

When hair is wet bonds in the hair are broken by a physical change. After the hair has dried, those bonds are reformed in a different shape. These bonds will hold the shape for quite some time or until the hair is wet again.

This is why women did not wash their hair everyday or even every other day. It was a time-consuming process to get some of these styles and washing it out made all the work in vain. Strong humidity can also relax the curl faster.

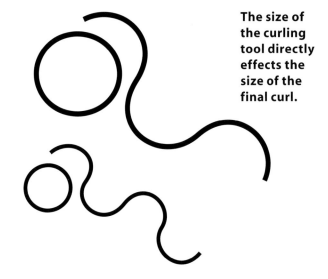

The size of the curling tool directly effects the size of the final curl.

Soft Roller

Soft rollers are a helpful roller for doing a wet set. Similar in concept to a rag roller, they are great if you want to sleep more comfortably while hair dries. But keep in mind that because air cannot circulate around the hair as well, they can take longer to dry.

1. To keep the ends more controlled while rolling, end wraps are useful. End wraps are made of a thin tissue material that holds together when wet. Fold the end wrap in half and insert the hair between each side. Pull the end wrap down until it covers the ends of the hair.

2 and **3.** Roll the hair as you would with any other roller. The ends have wire to fasten together.

1

2

3

4

Steam Setter

1

2

Steam Setters use both heat and water combined for a longer lasting curl. The curl does not last as long as a wet set but, for hair that does not take well to hot rollers, they are useful.

1. End wraps help control the ends of hair on the sponge surface of steam rollers.

2 and **3.** Wrap the ends over the roller and roll the hair to the scalp. It is important to move quickly with these types of rollers. The hot steam can cool very quickly and the curl will not take as well.

4. The fastening tool is a cap that snaps over the roller. For a better set, hold the cap over the steam dispenser for a few seconds before putting it on the roller. The heat and moisture will permeate through the top layer of hair.

5 and **6.** Steam setters can replace hot rollers for a basic set that is used in many of the hairstyles created in the book.

3

4

5

6

Velcro Roller

Velcro rollers use the locking technology of Velcro to hold the hair on the roller and prevent it from unraveling. Using pins and clips to hold a curl in place while drying can dent the hair. And that dent can still be seen after the hair is dry. With velcro, no clips or pins are usually needed.

The biggest difference between using a roller and using pin curls is the base of the hair. Rollers lift the hair away from the scalp, while pin curls keep the curl close to the scalp.

1. Velcro rollers have a **Base Direction** just like hot rollers or a curling iron. For an **Off-Base Curl**, hold the hair at a 45° angle towards the wrapping direction.

2. The **Off-Base Curl** roller sits away from the base of the hair.

3. The resulting curl has less volume, but the curl is strong and holds its shape well.

4. An **On-Base Curl** starts at a 45° angle away from the direction the hair is rolled.

5. The roller sits on top of the base of the hair to dry.

6. The curl from an On-Base velcro roller wet set is very full and strong. This method is a great way to get the big full volume of hairstyles from the 1960s. The wet set withstands the working and teasing needed to get the bouffant full.

1

2

3

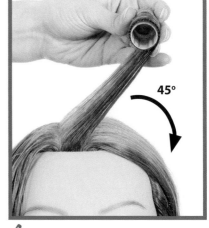

4

5

6

The Pin Curl

1

2

3

The most popular hairstyles in the past usually used a pin curl. A **Pin Curl** is the word used for any curl that is formed and held in place by a hairpin. The next several pages cover important considerations when choosing the pin curl wrapping method.

Its size and wrapping methods vary, but be careful not to pull the hair perpendicular out from the head. The curl will be much more manageable if it pulled parallel with the scalp while wrapping.

1 and **2.** First "ribbon" the hair between your thumb and the comb so the strands are straight and tense.

3, 4, and **5.** Choose what size the curl will be and wrap it around something, like your finger, to get the round shape. Slip the hair off of the finger to roll it toward the scalp. With some practice, you will be able to form a pin curl by just connecting the end of the hair to the hair strands and forming the curl free-hand.

6. Roll the pin curl towards the scalp. Keep the hair held snugly between your thumbs and index finger.

7 and **8.** The finished pin curl sits against the scalp and a hairpin is inserted to hold it in place.

8

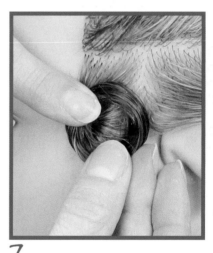

7

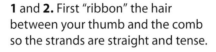

5

6

4

End Control

1 and **2.** A tip for better end control when pin curling is to start the curl part way from the ends.

3. Once you have reached a full circle, take the end in your fingers.

4 and **5.** Tuck the end into the middle of the curl and hold together, while you move the forming of the curl up toward to scalp.

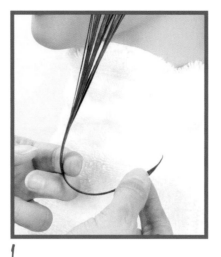

1

2

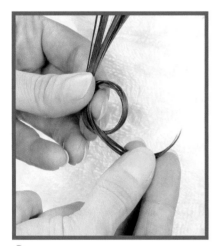

3

4

5

End Wraps

If having trouble with the ends staying put while trying to wrap a pin curl, end wraps can be helpful. First make sure that the hair is wet enough and enough shaping lotion has been used before resorting to end wraps .

If still having trouble, cut a wrap in half and fold that piece in half. Insert the hair in the folded wrap and pull it to cover the ends. Wrap the paper around until it is the same width as the hair strand. Then roll the curl.

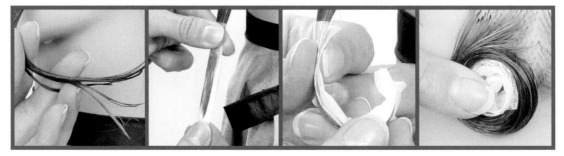

Pinning Pin Curls

1. Hairpins are the most common way of holding a pin curl in place to dry. Turn the hairpin so that one prong will slide in between the curl and the scalp. The other prong will slip over the top of the curl.

It is not very often that one hairpin is enough to hold. Crisscross hairpins through the curl until it holds itself up. Two pins are usually enough, but add as many as are needed.

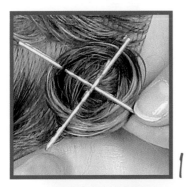

2. Double Prong Clips with a gap near the hinge work nicely on larger pin curls. Spread the tongs so that the prongs on the bottom of the clip slip in between the curl and the scalp. Push the clip all the way through until the side of the pin curl fits snugly at the gapped end of the clip.

Pin Curl Sizes

Shown here are different ways to measure out the size of the pin curl to use.

3. Wrap the hair around an index finger for a small pin curl.

4. Wrap the hair around the thumb for a medium-size pin curl.

5. Wrap the hair around two fingers for a larger pin curl.

6 and **7.** Shown is the effect of using these different sizes. Note that the base size chosen corresponds with to the size of the curl. Keep in mind that for larger pin curls, drying time increases.

Uniformity of the curl size is important . Each element in a style using pin curls should be made of the same size of curl. This ensures that the element combs out properly and the curls lay together nicely.

Pin Curl Direction

The **Direction** of a curl refers to the direction the curl itself winds. Most often it is referred to as clockwise or counterclockwise.

The curl used depends greatly on the desired effect. Many curls around each other that go the same direction tend to curl into each other. When the curls alternate they tend to fluff away from each other. In the case of a skip wave, shown in the next chapter, the alternating rows of pin curls fit into each other to form a wave.

In a clockwise curl, shown on the right, the hair winds in the same direction as the hands on a clock, to the right. Regardless of the direction of the base, the hair winds clockwise.

If the clockwise curl is on the right side of the head, the hair winds toward the face and is often referred to as a forward curl because of its apparent forward motion.

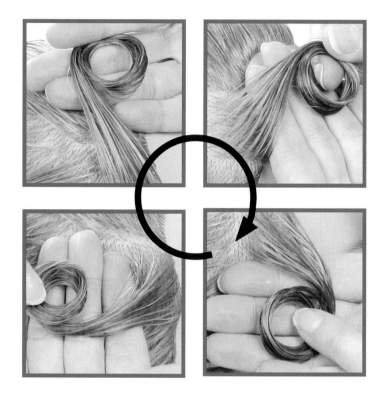

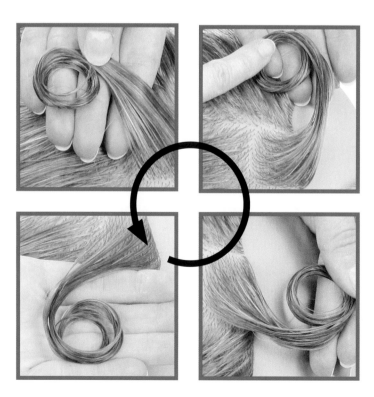

If it is on the left side of the head, it winds away from the face and is referred to as a reverse curl.

In a counterclockwise curl, shown on the left, the hair winds in the opposite direction of the hands on a clock, to the left. Regardless of the direction the base of the hair is pulled, the hair winds counterclockwise.

If the curl is on the left side of the head, the hair winds toward the face and is often referred to as a forward curl because of its apparent forward motion. If it is on the right side of the head, it winds away from the face and is referred to as a reverse curl.

Try wrapping pin curls in different directions around the head and note which direction they go and how they might be described.

Pin Curl Pivot Point

The **Pivot Point** of the curl refers to where the hair section "breaks" at the scalp in relation to the base of the curl. It has a great effect on how the curl lies when it is brushed out.

1. This image shows a curl with a proper pivot point. The hair section is directed and rolled on a diagonal compared to the direction the finished curl will lay. The final curl is intended to lie straight down.

2. This image shows an improper pivot point. Reasoning says that a curl that will hang down should be pulled down for wrapping and have a pivot point at the bottom, but that is incorrect.

3. The two curls with two different pivot points are pinned to dry.

4. The curl with the pivot point on the diagonal lies straight down. The curl with the pivot point at the bottom veers off to the side.

1

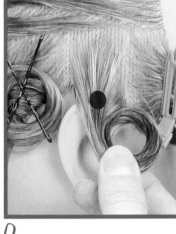

2

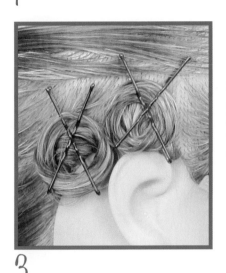

3

4

Base Shape

Base Shape refers to the shape of the base of the hair used in a pin curl. A rattail comb is the easiest way to section out the hair and keep control of the shape.

1. Base shape has the greatest effect at the hairline of the face. It is recommended that an alternating triangle base shape be used here. After the hair dries and is brushed out, the triangle shape camouflages the parts between each pin curl. If a square pin curl is used, the part between each one after it dries is more obvious.

2. Throughout the rest of a pin curl set a square can be used for the base shape. It is the easiest to measure out evenly and keep uniform.

3. Often old magazines and books will refer to a c-shaping. This is a base shaped like the back of a C. If doing a pin curl set on someone else, the c-shaping is easy. But if doing pin curls on your own head, the c-shaping is hard to keep uniform.

4. These pin curls have been set in a series of reverse curls, which we know from the information on the previous pages is a counterclockwise curl when it is on the right side of the head. The sections were pulled up and to the left to get started. Each vertical row is set with different base shapes.

5. When this set is brushed out loosely, there are no gaps at the hairline. The uniform direction of each curl allows the curls to form into each other.

1

2

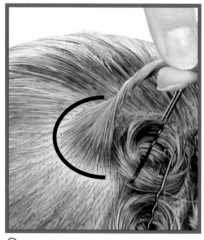

3

4

5

Base Placement

Base Placement is a lot like base direction for rollers. It refers to where the pin curl sits on the base of the hair from which it was rolled.

On-base pin curls have the least amount of movement at the scalp after drying and brushing out. It has a tendency to kink at the scalp because in order to get the curl so far over the base, some of the hair must literally be folded.

Half On-Base pin curls have a medium amount of movement at the scalp after dried and brushed out. It offers the most manageable option with the most curl. When it is brushed out it is smooth and curly throughout the entire strand of hair.

Off-Base pin curls have the most movement at the scalp after drying and brushing out. But the hair closest to the scalp ends up straight because it was not formed into the curl shape with the rest of the hair.

For all of these reasons, the **Half On-Base** placement is the most flattering for most styles.

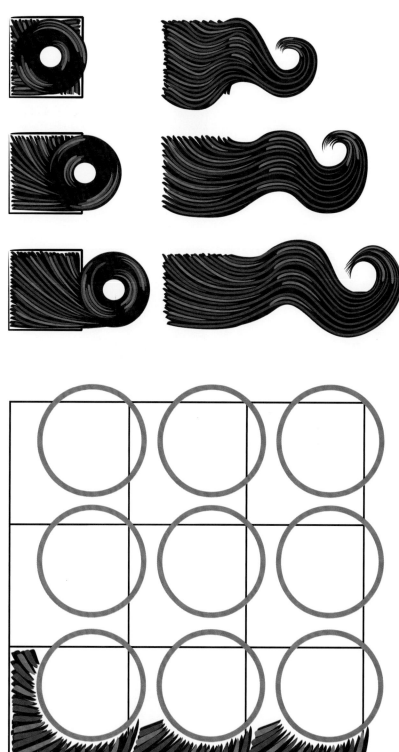

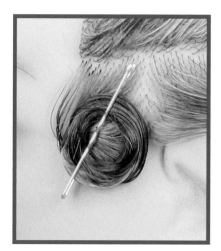

Pullout Direction

Another technique that has an effect on what the dried style looks like is the direction the hair is pulled out of the pin curl. There are only two options and both have their place in a pin curl set.

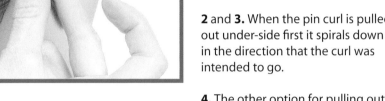

1. When the hair needs to stay close to the head for a style that is more flat or for brushing out waves this is the best way to pull the curl out of place for combing out. It stays close to the head and lies the best. Let your index finger reach up underneath the curl to pull the under side of the curl out first.

2 and **3.** When the pin curl is pulled out under-side first it spirals down in the direction that the curl was intended to go.

4. The other option for pulling out the pin curl is to grab the outside of the curl and pull it directly away from the scalp.

5. The result is a curl that stands away from the head and may be less manageable for pin curl waves. It is, however, a great option for a full pin curl fluff or cascades of curls that do not necessarily need to lie well with each subsequent row. It adds fullness to hair that is fine, but maybe too much fullness to very thick hair.

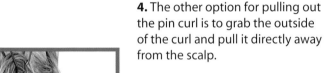

Stand-up Pin Curl

The stand-up pin curl is similar to a roller effect, but mimics natural curl and there is less of a chance of roller marks.

1. Pull the hair diagonally out opposite of the direction of the roll for an on-base curl. For this set, the hair is rolled toward the face at a diagonal so that after it dries and is brushed, it will wave forward.

2. Pin it in place with a single prong clip for drying.

3. The base shapes of these curls were set in triangles to avoid gaps.

4. Brush out for a great pompadour.

1

2

3

4

Combing Out

Books and magazines of the past sometimes refer to it as the comb out or brush out. They all refer to styling the hair after the curl is created. Think of the curled hair as clay and your comb or brush as the sculpting tool. Use the combs and brushes to sculpt the hair into the final shape.

Move the comb or brush in the same direction that you want the hair to go. If a wave is desired, the comb has to move in a wave pattern while combing. In some cases, as in a dried wet set, the hair will have such a strong hold that extra work will be required to sculpt it into the desired shape. At first brush, it will feel like it was done wrong. The curl will be so strong, but extra brushing and a light pomade will tame it and relax it. It will not go into the shape you want without guidance and a little force from you. Show the hair you are the boss, and it will do what you tell it with the comb as long as the correct curl was created in the first place.

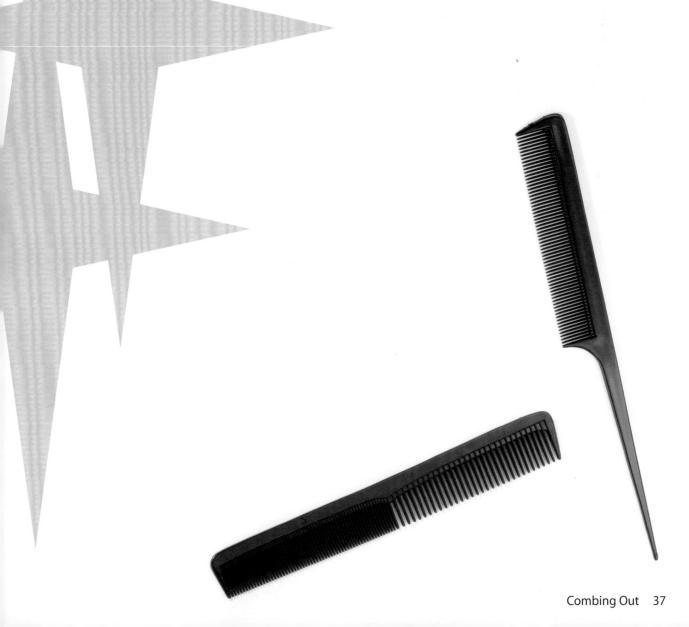

Victory Rolls

Victory Rolls have come to be a staple in a vintage look. Most associated with the 1940s, anytime dry hair is rolled into a shape and the opening can be seen, it can be considered a victory roll.

They are a fun and easy way to get a vintage look. If your hair is straight, put it in hot rollers first to get some bend and fullness into it. The hair will be easier to control and roll with some curl in it.

What you will need: hot rollers and clips, thermal spray, styling comb of choice, styling brush, bobby pins, hairspray, pomade

1. Set the hair in hot rollers and let cool. Hair can be slippery and if hair is too fine, the rolls may look skimpy. For this reason, back brushingor teasing is helpful. It adds locking power to the roll and fullness for high impact. Hold the entire piece that will be rolled up in the direction it will be rolled. Use a brush or comb to tease gently.

2. Then use a comb to smooth out the hair that will be on the outside of the roll. Spray a little hairspray on the hair to hold on to what was just formed.

3. This is where the bend from the hot rollers comes in handy. Allow the ends that now curl to curl into themselves.

4. This style works nicely when the ends of the hair are actually hidden inside the roll. It creates support in the style and staying power.

5. Hide large bobby pins inside the roll to attach to the hair at the scalp.

3

4

5

6

6. The victory roll can be made any size. Traditionally, it sits on top of the head facing forward, but experiment with different directions and placement. See the Final Styles section of the book for creative things to do with victory rolls.

7 and **8.** If it is not desired to see through the roll, gently insert a comb at the side of the roll and shift the hair back until the side of the roll is lyng flat against the hair.

9. Insert a couple of small bobby pins where the hair has been pressed against the head to hold a beautiful swoop.

10. Victory rolls can be created with any amount of hair desired. For this demonstration, very large pieces have been used, but breaking it up into smaller, more manageable pieces makes for good practice.

11. The second section of hair is rolled back, but held at a diagonal to center the roll. Also experiment with the direction that the section of hair is pulled to achieve different placement. Notice the first roll was pulled straight up for its base placement.

7

8

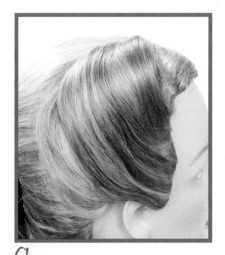

9

10

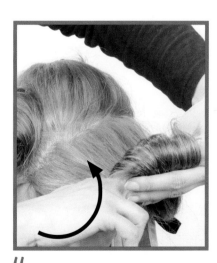

11

Pompadour

A pompadour can be many things. It is, essentially, a full rounded hair form above the forehead. It can be curly or mimic a victory roll. The key is the height. As with a victory roll, hot rollers will give the hair bend for more manageability.

What you will need: hot rollers and clips, thermal spray, styling comb of choice, bobby pins, hairspray, pomade

1. Set the hair in hot rollers and let cool. After removal, section off a triangular shape of hair that tapers toward the back. Tease the hair a little to lock it for hold and create fullness.

2. Begin rolling the section ends first towards the back of the head until it is sitting on its base.

3. Insert large bobby pins inside the roll to hide them.

4. Use hairspray, pomade, and comb teeth to smooth hair back and clean up fly-aways.

5. To fan the hair around the shape of the face, gently insert a comb into the roll and pull the hair around the forehead to the sides of the forehead.

6. Insert small hairpins where the hair now touches the scalp to hold in place.

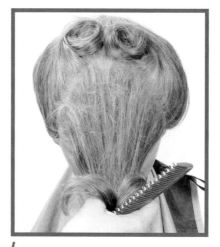

1

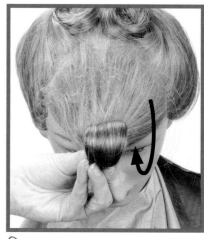

2

3

4

5

6

Rat Filler

If you have ever seen a set of vanity tools at an antique store, there was probably this strange little box that looked like a powder container. But for some reason it had a hole in the top of it. Well, that doesn't make sense! Wouldn't the powder get everywhere?

Obviously, it was not for powder. Women saved the hair they brushed out sitting at the vanity and placed it in a hair receiver.

The hair was saved for many reasons, including the making of jewelry chains. Another helpful use was for a rat filler.

A rat filler "fills" in where the hair needs help. If the hair is not long enough or too fine to give a roll fullness, a rat filler comes to the rescue.

What you will need: your own hair that you have collected or inexpensive sterilized hair extensions from your local beauty supply, an invisible hairnet, bobby pins

1. Tease and wad the hair into a cylinder shaped ball.

2. Wrap the hairnet around the rat.

3 and **4.** Then begin wrapping the hair around the rat and roll it into the desired look. Pin in place.

5. The finished roll is full and stable.

1

2

3

4

5

✦ Finger Wave ✦

Finger waves are most associated with styles of the 1920s and early 1930s. The wave in hair continued its popularity through the 1950s, but was created with pin curls for a fuller, more natural look.

The Combing Out section also includes directions for waves with pin curls, but before jumping ahead, it is highly suggested that finger waves are practiced. They are the best practice for understanding and perfecting waves from pin curl sets.

What you will need: water, shaping lotion, styling comb, hood hair dryer

Prep the hair by getting it very wet and putting a lot of styling lotion in it. This style requires the most pliable hair. It should be dripping wet. This means that it will also take a long time to dry, which is why a hooded hair dryer is suggested.

1. Start by combing the hair back at a diagonal. This will be the beginning of the first wave. Finger waves are easiest when using the wide tooth section of the comb.

2. Place your index finger FIRMLY on top of this hair. The hold must be firm enough to hold the hair in place while you comb the hair below the finger in the opposite direction.

3. Comb the hair below the finger at a diagonal toward the face. This has started the first wave.

4. Insert the teeth of the comb firmly into the hair a quarter inch below the finger and press up and to the right towards the finger. This begins the ridge of the wave. It may take a few pressings to get the hair up against the finger.

1

2

3

4

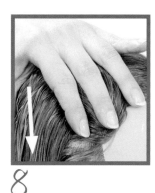

5

6

7

8

5. Replace the position of the index finger with the middle finger and place the index finger on the other side of the ridge, pinching the newly-formed ridge between the fingers. Then comb the hair back at a diagonal again. Make sure that your fingers are firm against the head to keep the hair from pulling.

6. Move the position of your fingers down one more step, with the ring finger taking the position of the middle finger, etc. The index finger is not yet placed back against the head.

7. Insert the teeth of the comb again firmly and press the hair up and back towards the middle finger to create the next ridge.

8. Put your index finger against the head again firmly and pinch the new ridge between the fingers to define it. Comb the hair underneath in a forward diagonal direction towards the face.

9

10

11

12

9. Move the fingers down another step. If following correctly, there is now an exposed wave and ridge at the top of the head. Press the teeth of comb firmly into the hair again and press the hair up and to the right to form what is now the third ridge.

10. Place the index finger down firmly on the head and pinch the new ridge between the index and middle finger. Comb the lower hair at a diagonal back away from the face.

11. There are now three waves with three ridges.

12. And the hairstyle has reached the bottom of the hairline. Finger waves are best kept on the scalp of the head. If the hair is longer than the hairline, try pin curling the ends gently to avoid pulling out what was just waved.

1 *2* *3* *4*

1. A tip in helping hold the finger waves ridge sharp is waving clips. First, form the ridges in the finger wave as best you can.

2. At some beauty supply stores you can still find these clips that look like long thin hair clips. They have holes along the side for more air circulation while drying. Be careful when sitting under a dryer with these in your hair. The metal can heat up fast.

3. The clip clamps over the ridge and pinches it to define more and hold.

4. Finger waves, pin curls, and spit curls are set wet and are much like a sculpture. Sometimes many tools are needed to hold the wet hair in place while it dries.

1 *2* *3* *4*

Spit Curl

The spit curl had its most popular time in the 1920s and early 1930s. But a curl that sits on the face has been around for centuries.

1. The spit curl is best created when the hair is wet. Form a pin curl by directing the hair as close to the face as possible.

2. Hair tape is a soft hold tape that sticks enough to hold the curl in place while it dries.

3 and **4.** Once the curls have dried, use a strong gel and apply it to the skin lightly. Then press the curl onto the gel coated spot.

✦ Pin Curl Wave ✦

Waves created with pin curls were popular from the 1930s through the 1950s. They are soft and beautiful and easier than you might think once the basic concept is understood. Hopefully, finger waves on the previous pages were practiced even a little before jumping to pin curl waves. It is the best way to understand the concepts laid out here and get the fingers trained for waves.

The beauty of this soft wave is that it is so diverse in its possible applications. Practicing combing out this wave adds possibilities to every style that has a curl in it. That includes styles created with the curling iron, hot rollers, velcro or soft rollers. Anytime there is a uniform curl in the hair, it can be brushed or combed into a wave.

Of course, the strength of a wet set lends itself to this style as it can withstand the brush out without losing the tightness of the curl too much. Here is a quick introduction to the importance of the curl consistency.

What you will need: water, shaping lotion, rattail comb, hairpins, hooded hair dryer, thin brush

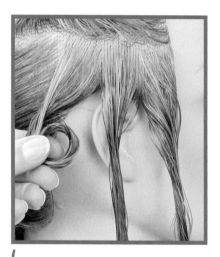

1

2

1 and **2.** Prep the hair using the steps on page 12. Wet set a row of 3 pin curls that are a consistent size and direction. Refer to The Curl section on proper pin curl rolling for the best results.

3. Pull the curls down so they rotate into the scalp and lay flat. Refer to page 32 for more information.

4 and **5.** Brush the hair section several times on top and underneath . If the hair was wet enough and allowed to dry, the hair will keep its curl, but relax enough to form into a wave.

3

4

5

Horizontal Pin Curl Wave

Moving on to a larger section, more pin curls are created in an alternating set called a skip wave. The hair is rolled in different directions in each row to "skip" over each other.

What you will need: water, shaping lotion, hairpins, rattail comb, hooded hair dryer, thin brush or pocket brush, duckbill clips, hairspray, pomade

1. As laid out in The Curl section, the pin curls at the hairline by the face should have triangular bases to camouflage gaps. Prep the hair using the steps on page 12.

2. The first pin curl is a reverse clockwise curl. The pivot point is on the bottom right of the base because the curl needs to fall down straight for the wave to work.

3. Each subsequent pin curl above it alternates direction and pivot point to create the skip. The middle curl is a forward counterclockwise curl with the pivot point on the bottom left of the base, the exact opposite of the curl above and below it.

4. Continue to set the curls for the bottom row. They are all reverse clockwise curls with a pivot point on the bottom right corner of the base.

5. Move up to the second row that skips or alternates compared to the bottom row. Roll these curls into reverse counterclockwise curls with a pivot point at the bottom left corner of the base.

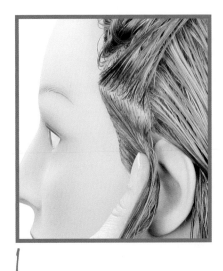

1

2

3

4

5

6

7

8

9

10

11

Horizontal Pin Curl Wave Cont.

6. The final top row mimics the row at the bottom with reverse clockwise pin curls with the pivot point at the bottom right corner of the base.

7. The result is a pin curl set of alternating rows.

8 and **9.** After the hair is dry, take out the pins and pull the pin curls down by first allowing them to rotate into the scalp as described on page 32. This will help control the wave and keep the hair from raising away from the head. It is also a good idea to take each row out at a time instead of everything at once.

10 and **11.** Using a brush with a lot of tension, begin brushing the hair several times. The hair needs to be relaxed a little to make it more manageable for combing into waves. If the hair was wet enough when set into the pin curls and thoroughly dry before brushing, the curl should withstand the rigorous brushing. Use pomade on your fingers for shine and control.

12. At first glance after this brushing, the sight is a little confusing. How is this mess going to turn into a wave?

13 and **14.** This is where the finger wave practice comes into play. Begin with the comb and start combing the hair into the direction of the first wave. This is a rounded motion.

15. Then place your index finger FIRMLY on the first wave. Then start moving the comb in the direction for the next wave. This will take a few strokes to get the hair working in the right direction.

16. Insert the teeth of the comb into the hair and press the hair up to start forming the first ridge.

17. Step your finger down so that your middle finger is firmly on top of the first wave and your index finger is holding the first ridge in place to keep it from being combed out. Comb the hair below vigorously to the right to start the forming of the next wave.

12

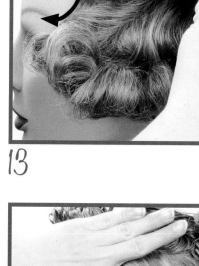

13

14

15

16

17

 18

 19

 20

 21

 22

 23

Horizontal Pin Curl Wave Cont.

18. After doing this motion, you will look at the wave and still say "This is a mess." It is not a mess. It is the beginning of a beautiful wave.

19. The wet set pin curl is very strong and needs to be made to go the direction you want it to go. Brush the hair out some more. But hang on to the hair to control it and keep it from frizzing.

20. Use a little hairspray often when working the hair. It wets the hair enough to make it more pliable without loosening the curl too much. It also is helpful to spray the brush with hairspray while working.

21. Move on to continue the motions. Comb the first wave in a circular motion.

22. Place the index finger on this first wave to hold it firmly in place and comb out the hair below the finger.

23. Insert the teeth of the comb into the hair just below the index finger and press the hair up to help define the first ridge.

24. Step the fingers down 2 steps so that the ring finger is firmly on top of the first wave and the middle finger is firmly on top of the second wave. This will help to pinch the first ridge between the fingers. Continue to comb and work the hair now moving the hair into a circular motion to create the next wave.

25. Place the index finger down on the next wave and continue to comb out the hair below the fingers.

26. The wave is finally starting to take shape nicely.

27. Continue to comb to get the hair in a uniform wave that fits together.

28. Use hairspray to make the hair more pliable and to hold the style.

29. Another helpful finisher for this wave is placing duckbill clips on the waves and hairspraying. When dry, remove the clips and the wave will be clean and beautiful. The finished wave is on the top of page 43.

24

25

26

27

28

29

Vertical Pin Curl Wave

The same techniques for creating the wave can be modified for different directions. The skip wave shown here will also utilize ridge curls. A ridge curl is a pin curl that is slightly shifted after being rolled to create a false ridge in the hair.

What you will need: water, shaping lotion, hairpins, rattail comb, hooded hair dryer, brush, duckbill clips, hairspray, pomade

1. Prep the hair using the steps on page 12. Because the wave will now wave backward on the head, the pin curl direction needs to roll backward. So the first front row of pin curls will all be reverse counterclockwise curls with the pivot point now at the top left corner of the base.

2. The pin curl is formed, but before it reaches the base, stop rolling. Shift the curl without turning it so that the hair at the hairline folds forward and creates a ridge.

3. Do the same for the entire front row of curls.

1

2

3

4

5

6

4 and **5.** The next row is only partly opposite. They are still reverse in that they are rolling away from the face, but they are now clockwise with their pivot point at the bottom left corner of the base. They are not formed into ridges like the first row.

6. After the hair has dried completely, brush out many times to relax the curl and make it more pliable to go the direction desired.

7, 8, 9, and **10.** Follow the same steps laid out on pages 44-47 to form the hair into a wave. This wave also takes a few comb-throughs to get the beautiful wave, but the results are worth it. Be sure to use hairspray to help in the forming and pomade for shine and control.

11. Because this style follows a line that defies gravity, bobby pins may be needed to hold it up and close to the head.

12. Again, try using a duckbill clip after the waves have been formed to get a nice, flat wave. Spray hairspray over it and let it dry before removing the clip. The finished style is on the previous page at the top.

7

8

9

10

11

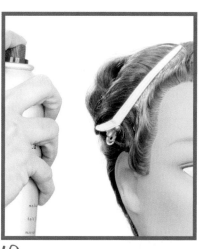

12

Marcel Wave with Wet Set

The Marcel Wave was invented by Marcel Grateau in the late 1800s. It revolutionized hairstyles for years after. He discovered that by turning his curling iron upside down, he could create a deep wave in the hair. This style combines an existing curl with the Marcel technique to create retro waves. The curling iron you use is directly related to the size of the curl you are working with.

What you will need: water, shaping lotion, small 1/2" velcro rollers, hood hair dryer, teasing/styling brush, 3/8" curling iron, hairspray

1

2

3

4

5

6

7

8

1. Wet set and dry your hair in small velcro rollers. A strong curl is created. This style can also be done with pin curls.

2 and **3.** Brush the hair out straight and hold the ends firmly in your fingers.

4. With a firm grasp on the ends, relax your hand back toward the scalp slowly with your other hand helping to control the curled piece of hair. As the hair relaxes the wave will start to show itself and a ridge will appear. At this point the hair would curl back, but keep hold of the ends to make sure the hair does not bounce back.

5. With a 3/8" curling iron heated and turned upside down, insert the iron so the shell goes under the piece of hair and the edge of the shell connects to the hair where the ridge is present.

6 and **7.** Let the upside down iron clamp down on the hair. It will take a little practice to get a feel for where the iron should be to catch the ridge at the right angle. For added direction, pull the curling iron and the hair in opposite directions.

8. Repeat the steps down the hair shaft alternating the direction of the pull to get a wave.

Marcel Wave with Curling Iron

The same techniques for the Marcel Wave can be applied to a dry style with a curling iron.

What you will need: thermal spray, curling iron of choice, styling comb, hairspray

1. With thermal spray for protection and stability, curl a section of hair.

2 and **3.** Comb the hair out straight and hold the ends firmly with fingers.

4. With a firm grasp on the ends, relax your hand back toward the scalp slowly with you other hand helping to control the curled piece of hair. As the hair relaxes the wave will start to show itself and a ridge will appear.

5 and **6.** With the same curling iron turned upside down, insert the iron so the shell goes under the piece of hair and the edge of the shell connects to the hair where the ridge is present. For added emphasis, pull the curling iron and the hair in opposite directions. Repeat the steps down the shaft.

1

2

3

4

5

6

✦ Final Styles ✦

Hollywood has long been a primary influence on perceptions of beauty and style in America, especially when it comes to hair. Veronica Lake's peek-a-boo bang and Jean Harlow's bleached locks started powerful trends. Marlene Dietrich's high eyebrows and Theda Bara's "vamp" makeup, although eccentric, influenced the way young women pictured beauty. In the introduction you can find places to reference the many different styles these ladies wore.

In this section, you will find finished hairstyles inspired by many trends of the past. The first hairstyles use modern tools. As you work your way back, you will find more complicated styles using techniques of their day. Keep in mind that some curling methods can be replaced with others to suit your needs.

Hairstyles can also be combined or modified to suit your own hair thickness and length. Look through ALL the styles and techniques and see if something may apply to your hair and desired outcome. And above all, experiment and practice. The more you do, the more you will understand the methods, and the happier you will be with the results.

✦ The Vixen ✦

This hairstyle is quick and easy. The key to good results is using a thermal spray to protect the hair and help hold the curl. It is also important not to use too large a section of hair in the curling iron or it will not heat thoroughly and will loosen quickly. This style is great on any length, no matter how short or long, as long as it can get around a curling iron. This shape was very popular throughout the mid-twentieth century and was worn by many actresses, including Cleo Moore.

What you will need: small to medium curling iron, thermal spray, double prong clips, rattail comb, styling comb of choice, hairspray, pomade, duckbill clips

1

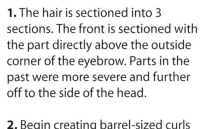
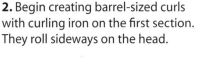
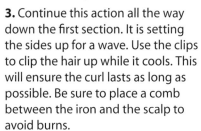
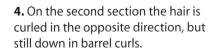

2

1. The hair is sectioned into 3 sections. The front is sectioned with the part directly above the outside corner of the eyebrow. Parts in the past were more severe and further off to the side of the head.

2. Begin creating barrel-sized curls with curling iron on the first section. They roll sideways on the head.

3. Continue this action all the way down the first section. It is setting the sides up for a wave. Use the clips to clip the hair up while it cools. This will ensure the curl lasts as long as possible. Be sure to place a comb between the iron and the scalp to avoid burns.

4. On the second section the hair is curled in the opposite direction, but still down in barrel curls.

3

4

5

6

7

8

9

10

11

12

13

5. The third section at the back of the head is curled down in a bricklay pattern and pinned up to cool.

6. Begin by taking down the lower curls of section 1 and combing them into a wave. Because the curling iron curl is more relaxed than a pin curl, it is easier to get the hair to wave, but it is still important to follow the steps laid out in the Combing Out section to understand the wave process.

7. Use hairspray to keep the hair pliable and hold the style.

8 and **9.** Continue with section 1, combing the hair into waves.

10. Comb the last two curls of section 1 up and over to get height and fullness above the forehead. Teasing can be used for more height.

11. Arrange the curls at the end as desired with pomade and hairspray. Then repeat steps 6-10 on section 2.

12 and **13.** Repeat steps 6-10 on section 3 on the back of the head. Arrange the hair in waves and hairspray for hold.

✦ Snood Style #1 ✦

The Snood has been around for centuries as a popular hair accessory. But in 1939, when Vivien Leigh sported it in the classic movie *Gone with the Wind*, it solidified its place as one of the most popular war-time accessories. The snood did a great job of protecting a woman's hair while she worked in the factories. See the resource section for places to find snoods today. If your hair is too short to fill a snood, curl the front section and replace the snood with a Rosie-type bandana. See the *Other Options* section of the book for bandana/scarf directions.

What you will need: small curling iron and hot rollers and clips, thermal spray, rattail comb, styling brush, pomade, hairspray, bobby pins, duckbill clips, snood

1

2

1. Section the hair into 2 sections. Section 1 includes all the hair at the front of the head and section 2 includes all of the hair on the back.

2. Section 2 can be set in hot rollers or a curling iron can be used to get some bend into the hair. This section of hair will be placed in the snood and only needs some bend to fit in the snood and lie nicely.

3. The right side of section 1 is curled with a curling iron up towards the center of the top of the head.

4. The left side of section 2 is curled up in the opposite direction towards the center of the top of the head.

3

4

5

6

5. Curl the entire front section of hair in this manner.

6. Get some pomade on your fingers and start separating out the curls created with the curling iron.

7. Take a square section of hair on top of the head and twist it at the scalp to create a base. Pin it in place. This will be the base to use for pinning subsequent pieces of hair up in the style.

8. Start rolling pieces of curl up to the center of the head. This is the beginning of what will be a curl fluff. Pin the pieces up with bobby pins.

9 and **10.** To help interlock the curls together, pull pieces of hair through each other and pin in place.

7

8

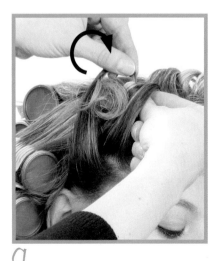

9

10

11

12

13

14

15

16

11. The effect is a rolling of waves that go up the head.

12. Take the rest of the pieces of hair and pin up into the curl fluff.

13. The final section that hangs down the middle of the forehead is pinned up, but not all the way above. This gives the appearance of a curly pompadour hanging over the forehead. Hairspray for hold.

14. Brush out the back section of the hair to put in the snood.

15. Snoods are often made of a knit material that stretches. Slip the snood over the entire back hair section.

16. Knit snoods have a tendency to slip off of the head, so pin it in place with bobby pins.

✦ Snood Style #2 ✦

This dramatic snood style is inspired by Betty Grable. Over her career, she wore many silhouettes that piled her hair high on her head, especially in the movies *Pin Up Girl* and *The Dolly Sisters*. I would encourage girls who have bangs to also try a style like this. The rolls can be placed on top of the bangs.

What you will need: medium hot rollers and clips, rattail comb, thermal spray, styling comb of choice, snood, bobby pins, pomade, hairspray

1. The hot rollers are set on-base, rolling down. On-base is important for volume in this style.

2. After the rollers have cooled, part out the back section of hair that falls behind the ears and put on the snood. Pin snood in place.

3. Section the front in 3 equal sections and start a series of victory rolls rolling in on the 2 outer sections. See page 38 for more detailed instructions on victory rolls.

4 and **5.** Part the middle section at a diagonal and roll and pin hair in smaller victory rolls.

✦ The Homemaker ✦

The key to this style is the direction that the rollers are rolled. The front two sections of hair at the sides are parted at a diagonal and rolled back toward the nape of the neck. This setting pattern encourages the hair to fall properly. An alternative to this style is to continue brushing the hair toward the face during step 9 until the curls form together and roll into a page boy shape.

What you will need: hot rollers and clips, medium curling iron, rattail comb, thermal spray, styling comb of choice, single prong clips, bobby pins, pomade, hairspray

1

2

1. Part the hair into 4 sections. The sides from the outer eyebrow down to the ears are the first 2 sections. The top section includes the area between the outer eyebrows and 3-4 inches back from the hairline. The fourth section is the hair on the back of the head.

2 and **3.** Begin by setting 3 hot rollers on each side of the front of the head. The rollers are rolled at a diagonal away from the face. See page 22 for more information on hot rollers.

4. The hair directly behind the ears and below is set in a basic roller set pattern on-base. This particular model has layers in her hair, so to work with layers that are too short for rollers, the hair above the occipital bone is curled using a medium size curling iron as a length curl. Use this curl to avoid volume at the crown and create a more authentic look. See page 21 for more information on length curls.

3

4

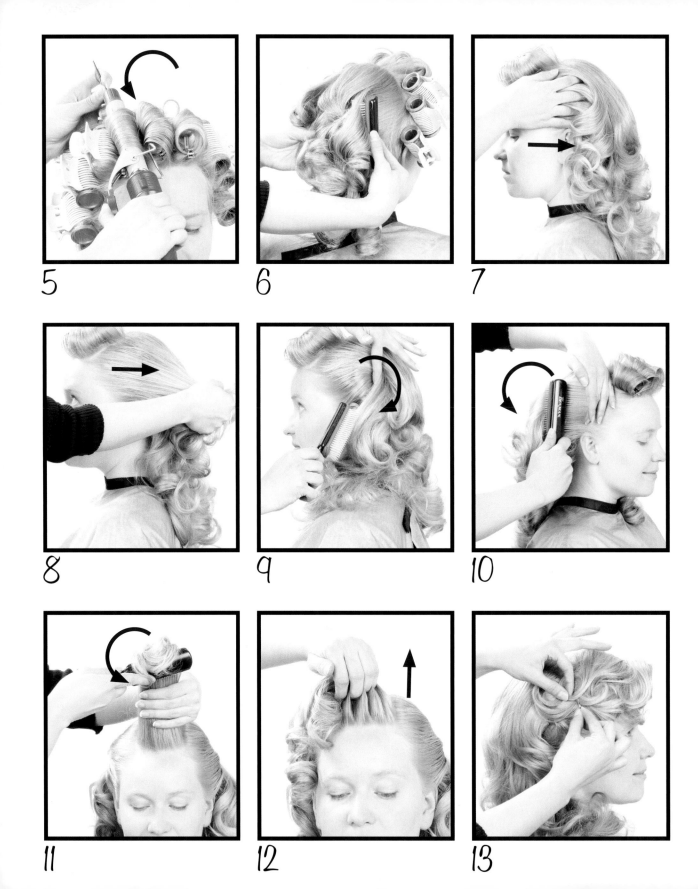

5

6

7

8

9

10

11

12

13

5. The section left is the top section. Using the medium curling iron, create on-base curls. Pin the curls in place to cool. The direction chosen is based on the desired way the hair should fall. Keep in mind that if the hair is curled in the opposite direction of the natural part and styled against the natural part, more volume is achieved above the forehead.

6. Unpin and brush through the back. Keep hand with pomade wrapped on the hair to control frizz.

7 and **8.** Take the rollers out of one side, but leave the iron curls on top of the head pinned and out of the way. The sides will be sculpted first. With a small amount of pomade coated on your palm, "comb" the hair back with your fingers pressing into the scalp. Do this a few times until the shape start to hold itself.

9. Using bobby pins, pin the sides back and gently brush some curls forward to wrap toward the face.

10. Repeat steps 7-9 on the other side.

11. Unpin the hair in the top section and brush the curls up and over to the side the hair will fall.

12. With a small amount of pomade, use your fingers to sculpt and lift in front for volume.

13. Form some small, dry pin curls and bobby pin in place on the sides. Hairspray for hold.

✦ '30s Fake Bob ✦

Spilling over from the bob that was so popular in the 1920s, the young girls that rebelled by cutting their hair boy-short and wearing boxy dresses were growing up and embracing feminine curls and curves again in the 1930s. But their finished styles stayed above the shoulders. This style to fake shorter hair can be done on any hair length. Longer hair just needs to be pinned up more underneath.

What you will need: small hot rollers and clips, thermal spray, rattail comb, pocket brush or styling comb of choice, bobby pins, hairspray, pomade

1

2

1. The front section of hair is parted above the outer point of the eyebrow. Using small hot rollers, set the front with each section rolling away from the part.

2. Part the back section behind the ears and pin up the hair at the crown to keep it out of the way. Set the lower section of hair using on-base curls. See page 23 for more information.

3. The section left at the crown is rolled off-base to leave the crown flat. If the crown is not left flat, there is a risk of getting a Shirley Temple effect with the curls being this small.

4. Begin taking the rollers out one at a time starting at the bottom of the largest front section and brushing each rolled piece out on its own. Be sure to coat a small amount of pomade on hands to control frizz. It is important to be patient and brush each section by itself. If the sections of hair are brushed together, they become too thick. This will lose the very wavy 1930s effect to a bigger 1950s look.

3

4

5

6

7

8

9

10

11

12

13

5 and **6.** Continue brushing one rolled section at a time with comb and some pomade on hands to control frizz. Hairspray while working.

7. Once the last 2 rollers at the top in the largest section of hair at the front are reached, brush the hair up and over to where the hair will fall.

8. Take the last roller out and brush it up and over.

9. Once it is lying in its general final spot, continue combing, being careful not to snag the other sections of hair that have been combed already.

10. Using the techniques starting on page 46, form this section into a wave using the brush and your fingers. Hairspray for hold.

11 and **12.** Remove the hot rollers from the other smaller side section and brush the hair, using pomade on your hands for control.

13. Remove the rollers and brush the back section of hair down, not out. Try to avoid creating too much volume in the curls.

14 and **15.** Take the hair hanging below the nape of the neck and turn it under. Pin the hair up in place with bobby pins to create shorter hair appearance.

✦ '50s Fake Bob ✦

This style follows the same idea behind the '30s Fake Bob on page 72. But the curl is larger and more smooth. In the 1950s, curl was more relaxed and there was less pressure for perfect waves. This style to fake shorter hair can be done on any hair length. Longer hair just needs to be pinned up more underneath.

What you will need: medium hot rollers and clips, thermal spray, rattail comb, styling comb of choice, bobby pins, hairspray, pomade

1

2

1. The hair is set in the same pattern it will lie in the finished style. The parting is at the outer point of the eyebrow. Using thermal spray, set the rollers on-base with the direction going back at an angle. See page 22 for hot roller information.

2. Set the entire top section this way.

3. Set the rest of the hair on-base in a basic roller set pattern.

4. Take all of the rollers out and comb/brush the hair down using pomade on hands to control frizz and direct the hair.

3

4

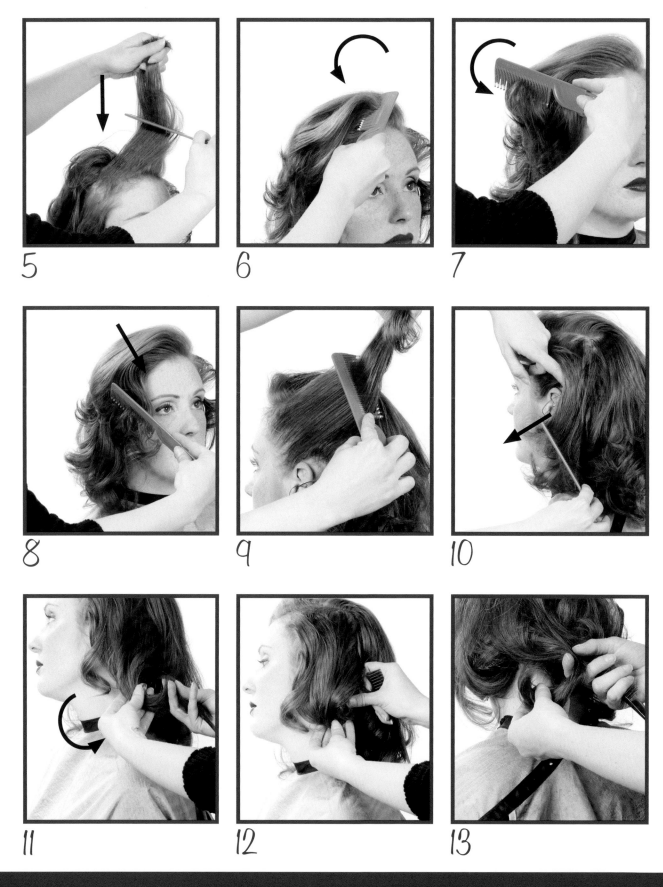

5

6

7

8

9

10

11

12

13

5. Pull up a large section at the top and tease the hair for added fullness.

6 and **7.** Start the direction of combing the top so that it moves at a diagonal toward the back of the ear.

8. Once the side is reached start the comb action toward the face. This creates a curve.

9. Comb the smaller side section back and hairspray.

10. Then, holding the top back, round the bottom of the hair section toward the face.

11 and **12.** This section that has just been rounded toward the face is pinned up underneath the ear. To get a round effect all the way around the head, this style is pinned up in sections, unlike the '30s Style Bob that is pinned up in one piece.

13 and **14.** Repeat pinning with a section of hair at the nape of the neck.

15 and **16.** Repeat pinning with the section of hair left on the other side of the head. Hairspray for hold.

14

15

16

✦ The Page Boy ✦

The page boy is a style that dates back centuries, but enjoyed a comeback during the 1940s and 1950s. The hair needs to be long enough to roll at least one-and-a-half times under to be pinned in place. It can roll many more times for someone who wants to make their longer hair appear shorter.

What you will need: hot rollers and clips, thermal spray, rattail comb, styling comb of choice, styling brush, hair combs, bobby pins, hairspray, pomade

1. Volume at the scalp is not desired for this style, so the rollers are set off-base. Large hot rollers are used to get the ends to turn under, but a curl is not what is desired. See page 23.

2. Tease hair underneath and comb all of the hair under in the back and on the sides. Hairspray to help hold the shape. This would also be an appropriate place to use a rat filler from page 41.

3. Hide pins underneath and inside the style.

4. Insert a hair comb by using it to comb the hair back at the sides and then pressing forward to lock it in place.

5. Smooth hair with a comb and pomade toward the face and under to the neck. Hairspray for hold.

1

2

3

4

5

✦ Pompadour Twirl ✦

For this hairstyle, the hair on the back of the head can be any length. As long as it is long enough to fit around a curling iron, you will still be able to get the same curl fluff effect. Depending on the thickness and length of the front of the hair, the pompadour may be smaller or larger, but regardless, it will be a fun style. The shape and form of this style is inspired by an Alberto Vargas pin-up painting.

What you will need: small curling iron and/or hot rollers and clips, thermal spray, rattail comb, single prong clips, styling comb of choice, bobby pins, hairspray, pomade, large clips

1

2

1. The hair is separated into 2 sections. The front of the head is section 1 and the back of the head is section 2.

2. The front can be put in either hot rollers or a medium curling iron can be used to achieve a bend in the hair. It will make the process of creating the pompadour easier.

3 and **4.** The entire back section of the hair will be curled with a 3/8" curling iron. The goal is to get a small tight curl without waiting for a pin curl set to dry. Start by clipping up the hair and leaving a small thin section at the bottom down for curling. Take a small square of hair and curl it thoroughly on-base with a curling iron. Be sure to keep a comb between the iron and the scalp for protection. Pin curls up with clips to cool.

3

4

5

6

7

8

9

10

11

12

13

5. Continue this row across. Then take down the next 2 rows of hair and curl in the same way. This completes curling the hair behind the ears.

6 and **7.** The next row is curled off-base. The reason is that the back of this style will mimic the 1940s trend of only curling the hair around the hairline. So as you work your way up, the base of the curl will get longer and longer.

8. When you reach the top, the base of hair left out of the curling iron to stay straight has reached 3 inches.

9. The effect is a flat crown with curl at the bottom.

10. Remove the clips holding the hair up and use a styling comb with large teeth to comb out the curl. Keeping your hand wrapped around the hair with pomade on your fingers while you comb will cut down on frizz.

11 and **12.** Now moving to the front section of hair, put a diagonal part through it to separate the hair in 2 sections. After some teasing to add volume, roll one section around much the same way you would create a victory roll, only allow the large curl to lay against the head.

13. Hold it loosely in place and pin. Try not to pull or push too tightly on these front elements. They are meant to be full. Let the ends of the section roll into their own separate pin curls and pin in place.

14 and **15.** After teasing the second front piece for fullness, pull it up and allow it to fall over the center of the top of the head. Pin the roll in place trying to hide the bobby pins underneath and inside the style. Hairspray for hold.

14

15

✦Happy Pompadour✦

At first glance, this style looks like it requires a lot of hair, but it can be done on shorter hair as well. It is called the Happy Pompadour in this book thanks to the reflection created in the hair in the shape of a smile. The size of this rounded pompadour is determined by how tight the front is rolled. Rita Hayworth wears this look on an even larger scale in a scene from *Covergirl,* with hairstyles created by movie hairstylist Helen Hunt.

What you will need: medium to large hot rollers and clips, thermal spray, rattail comb, styling comb of choice, bobby pins, ponytail holder, banana clip, pomade, hairspray

1

2

1. This hairstyle is broken up into 2 main sections. The first section is the hair surrounding the forehead. The second section includes everything else. Set the hair in on-base hot rollers. At the top, the second roller back is set to roll forward to avoid an indentation mark. The side rollers near the face are set at a diagonal rolling back. The purpose is for the hair at the hair line to set smoothly. Sometimes when rollers are set straight down at the hairline, the lower hair can get an indentation that shows in the finished style. See page 22 for more on hot rollers.

2. After the rollers have cooled, section out a triangle of hair that is as wide as the 2 outer points of the eyebrows and reaches a point where the head start to drop off in the back.

3. Put this section of hair in a small ponytail holder with the ponytail sitting close to the front of the hairline.

4. Tease this section to spread across the front of the face.

3

4

5

6

7

8

9

10

11

12

13

5. Then smooth the top and roll the hair under toward the forehead. Insert a bobby pin or 2 to help hold the roll. Pomade is very helpful in this style. Keep a light film on hands to keep hair under control.

6. Gently with both hands, spread the roll in a U-shape.

7. Hide bobby pins from the back inside the roll to hold it in place.

8. Part out one side section to create a victory roll. See page 38 for more information on creating victory rolls.

9 and **10.** The size of the victory roll should match the size of the opening of the front roll. Hold the hair high and roll it down toward the front roll, connecting the 2 together and pinning in place. Repeat these steps on the section on the other side of the head.

11. The back section of hair is held together with a horizontal banana clip. This clip is used to spread the hair, allowing it to be seen from the front. The clip can be decorated with flowers or ribbon.

12 and **13.** It is a personal preference on whether or not to leave the openings at the back visible. For a smoother transition from the front to the back, gently insert the teeth of the comb into the side of the victory roll. Then shift the comb back and toward the scalp so that the opening closes into the scalp. Pin and hairspray in place.

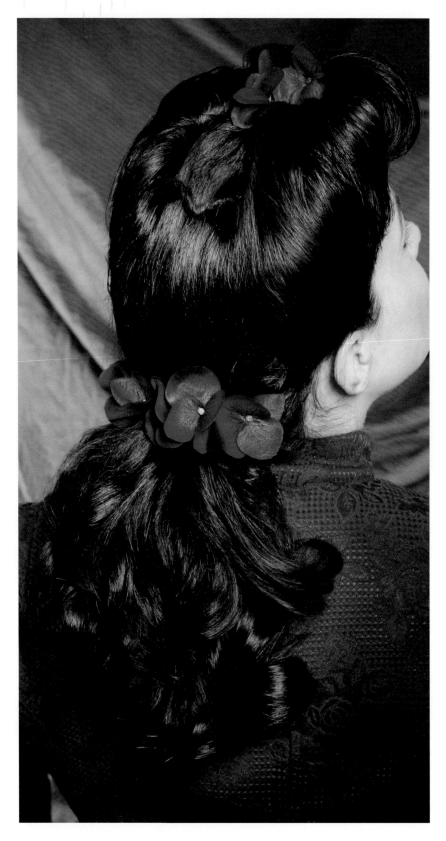

✦ Your Unique Pomp ✦

Pompadours can take on so many shapes. Their popularity for women in the 1940s inspired creativity. The creation of this pompadour is meant to open up the possibilities. Play with height and where the curls are placed. There are endless options.

What you will need: small curling iron, thermal spray, rattail comb, single prong clips, styling comb of choice, bobby pins, hairspray, pomade

1

2

1 and **2.** The hair for this style is curled in 2 sections. The front section includes all the hair in front of the back of the ears. Curl the hair forward toward the face. Pin it with clips while it cools for a stronger curl.

3. The back section is curled down toward the nape of the neck. To get the look of a flat crown, the hair is curled starting at the bottom with on-base curls. While working up in rows, the final row is curled in a length curl to avoid volume. See the Pompadour Twirl on page 82 for more information on this curl pattern.

4. Remove the clips and part a small triangle of hair out above the forehead. A triangle is used because it will be easier to cover the parting marks for a cleaner look.

3

4

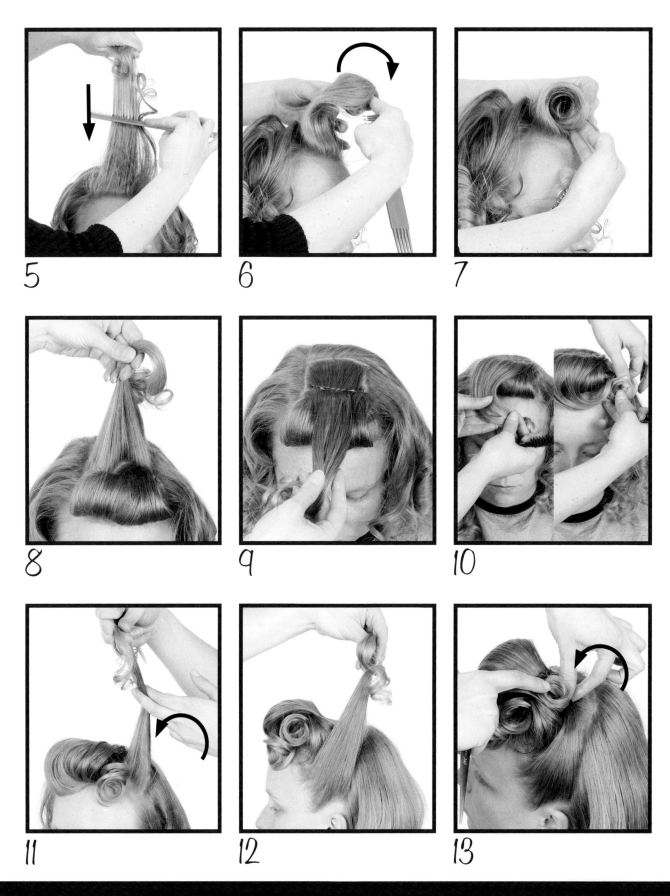

5

6

7

8

9

10

11

12

13

5. Tease the triangle section to desired fullness.

6 and **7.** Roll the section forward to create a base layer and pin in place with the bobby pins going inside the sides of the roll.

8. Then take another small section behind the roll. This is where the build begins. And this is where the creativity can begin. Experiment with hair placement.

9. Here, the hair is pulled forward over the first roll and bobby pinned down behind it to keep the pompadour effect.

10. Spread the hair across and to the side to create a wave and pin, allowing the curled ends to spread.

11. The next several steps involve small sections of hair sculpted into dry pin curls around the pompadour.

12, 13, 14, and **15.** Continue to set dry pin curls around the style as desired. In this case, curls are pinned on top of the bobby pins from step 9 to camouflage.

14

15

✦ The Pin-up ✦

This hairstyle is very buoyant and a lot of fun if going out dancing. Just a little shake and the hair will bounce all over. The model's layers are very long, so the style is designed to provide a cascade of curls all the way down the face. It is inspired by Doris Day's hair when her career was first blossoming in the late 1940s.

What you will need: small and medium curling irons, thermal spray, rattail comb, single prong clips, styling comb of choice, bobby pins, pomade, hairspray, duckbill clips

1

2

1. This hairstyle is broken up into 2 main sections. The first section is a small piece of hair above the forehead. The second section includes everything else.

2. Use a medium-sized curling iron and roll the first section back and pin in place to cool.

3. The rest of the hair is curled in the same way as The Pompadour Twirl on page 82 (refer back for more details). The goal is to create a flat crown area to mimic the style of the 1940s, the purpose of which was to make hat wearing easier. Curl the first 3 rows on-base with a small curling iron. The curls are to be very small and buoyant.

4. Be sure to place a comb between the curling iron and the scalp for protection. While working up the rows of the hairstyle, the base of hair that is not included in the curl gets longer and longer.

3

4

5

6

7

8

9

10

11

12

13

5. The finished curls are pinned up to cool. Notice that the curls on top of the head have long sections that were not included in the curling iron.

6. Unpin and comb through the curls with a wide tooth comb. Keep hand with pomade on fingers wrapped on the hair to control frizz.

7 and **8.** Take the small section curled in the beginning and tease the hair a little to create volume. Comb it backwards into a pompadour and pin in place.

9. Use hairspray and a comb to smooth the outside.

10. With pomade on your fingers, separate the curls toward the front of the face.

11. Take small sections of the curls around the face and pin them up.

12. Continue to pin to give the effect of a cascade of curls coming down the side of the face.

13. The back of the hairstyle is left alone. Hairspray for hold.

✦ Tiki Lounge ✦

The direction and steps of this hairstyle can be used on many lengths of hair to give the effect of shorter hair. Styles seen in old magazines give the appearance that the women had very short hair. That was the case sometimes, but often, to get the curl desired, there needed to be some length. Once it was curled, a lot of the length was lost. This hairstyle is inspired by Anne Baxter in *All About Eve* starring Bette Davis.

What you will need: small curling iron, rattail comb, single prong clips, thermal spray, pomade, hairspray, large and small bobby pins, large clips

1

2

1. This hairstyle is sectioned into what can best be described as a series of halos around the head. The hair is then curled downward. The reason for this is that when the style is then styled back in the opposite direction, it will create the full curl effect.

2 and **3.** Using a small curling iron, start working around the first halo and pin the hair in place to cool.

4. Continue until 3 halos of curls have been curled downward.

3

4

5

6

7

8

9

10

11

12

13

5. The small bit of hair left at the crown can be curled straight back.

6. With pomade on your fingers, finger through the curls down toward the floor to separate and add shine. The reason for the downward motion is to keep the crown area flat.

7 and **8.** Using large bobby pins that are the same color as the hair, create a crown around the hair that holds hair in the crown area flat and close to the scalp. The effect around the face is a curl fluff.

9 and **10.** Loosely grab hold of the free curls and pull them back over to cover the large bobby pins.

11. Use small bobby pins and insert in curls to hold in place.

12. Continue this around entire head until the front is reached and all of the large bobby pins have been covered.

13. Pull up on curls above the forehead and spray with hairspray to hold. Pin some to cover large bobby pins, but do not pin them all so that some can be left free. Hairspray for hold.

✦ Brigitte ✦

French film star Brigitte Bardot made this look popular in the early 1960s around the same time she was filming *A Very Private Affair*. The choucroute ("Sauerkraut") hairstyle got its name for the unkept, untamed similarity to piles of the sour cabbage. Bardot had very long hair, so for this style, extensions have been added for effect and to show options for using hair falls.

What you will need: medium hot rollers and clips, rattail comb, clip in hair extensions, ribbon, thermal spray, hairspray, pomade

1. Human hair extensions were used for their curling capabilities. Synthetic extensions can be curled with a very cool curling iron, but be careful. They melt if the iron is even 15° too hot. Start with the curling iron at 220° then work the temperature up little by little if you would like to try this with the less expensive synthetic extensions.

2. The first roller at the top of the head is rolled forward. This will set the split part bangs. But bangs are not needed for this style. You can still get the look with longer hair.

3. The rest are set in a basic on-base hot roller set.

4. Remove the rollers after cooling and gently brush the hair out. Hairspray to start adding texture and stick.

5 and **6.** With pomade on fingers, finger through the front section of hair and pull up on it to add texture and separate.

7. Part the front in the middle and comb lightly out and back.

8 and **9.** Tease the hair quite a bit at the crown and on the sides. The more height the better for this style.

10 and **11.** Loosely grab hold of the teased sections and pull back over the crown. No real smoothing of the top is done here.

12. Loosely grab side sections of the hairstyle and pull them back behind the head.

13. Using a ribbon, tie the sides back. Hairspray for hold.

✦ Jazz Singer ✦

In order to do this entire hairstyle, it is important that the hair at the nape of the neck is long enough that it can come up to the top of the head and roll over into a victory roll. This model has extensions, but that did not get in the way of getting her hair up. The clean, curly height of this style is inspired by many of singer Lena Horne's styles on stage.

What you will need: hot rollers and clips, thermal spray, rattail comb, styling comb of choice, hairspray, pomade, bobby pins, duckbill clips

1

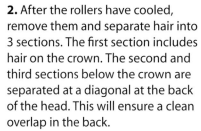

2

1. As explained on page 23, set the hair at the crown in small to medium hot rollers and the hair below in large hot rollers. A curl is desired on the top of the head, but the hair from the bottom to be set in rolls only needs to have bend to aid in direction.

2. After the rollers have cooled, remove them and separate hair into 3 sections. The first section includes hair on the crown. The second and third sections below the crown are separated at a diagonal at the back of the head. This will ensure a clean overlap in the back.

3 and **4.** Take the entire second section on the left side and pull up towards the crown. Use a styling comb to tease and smooth as need to create a victory roll. See page 36 for directions on creating a victory roll.

3

4

5

6

7

8

9

10

11

12

13

5. The victory roll is wide and placed above the outer corner of the eyebrow. When pinning the roll in place, insert bobby pins through the front of the roll. Do not yet pin the back of the roll. It needs to stay flexible to finish the back in step 9.

6, 7, and **8.** Take section 3 on the right side of the head and repeat steps 3-5 to create a victory roll on the right. Again, pin the roll through the front to keep the back flexible for step 9.

9. Gently take hold of the top of the roll on the right side of the head. Pull the hair loosely to the left to overlap the roll on the left. If grip is loose, it will allow the hair to fan itself and stay even across the gap. Gently separate the hair to put pins inside the style and hold in place. Then hairspray hair to cover gaps.

10. Get a little pomade on fingers and separate out the curls in section 1 of the hair. The curls on top can just sit on top with some hairspray or, if hair will not stay in place, hide a few bobby pins inside.

11. If you are having trouble covering the gap, pull some of the curls to hang down over to hide it.

12 and **13.** Hairspray for hold.

✦ For The Boys ✦

The back of this hairstyle is only meant to be a guide. The twisting of the hair can be done in many different directions . The idea is to mimic the pin curl look of so many up-do hairstyles of the 1940s and 1950s. These styles often took the form of large dry pin curls on the top of the head. If your hair is not long enough in the back to create this looks, try replacing it with a French twist or a bandana or scarf tied up to cover the back of the head.

What you will need: hot rollers and clips, small curling iron, thermal spray, rattail comb, pomade, hairspray, bobby pins, ponytail holder, duckbill clips

1

2

3

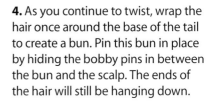

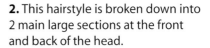

4

1. Set the hair in a basic roller set with large rollers. The hair does not need to be curly, but it will go in the direction of the victory rolls and twists much more easily if it has bend. Note that small hot rollers needed to be used above the forehead where the model has bangs that were too short for large rollers.

2. This hairstyle is broken down into 2 main large sections at the front and back of the head.

3. The back section is broken into 3 equal sized subsections. Put these subsections in ponytails. The middle tail is placed lower than the outside tails. This will create a U shape when the style is finished. Take the first tail and start twisting the hair.

4. As you continue to twist, wrap the hair once around the base of the tail to create a bun. Pin this bun in place by hiding the bobby pins in between the bun and the scalp. The ends of the hair will still be hanging down.

5

6

7

8

9

10

11

12

13

5. Do the same action to the other 2 ponytails.

6. Take the ends of the first bun and twist them.

7. Pull them up and let them loop towards the bun in middle.

8. Pin these new loops in place.

9. The appearance of this technique is that the hair is one piece that has been intertwined around itself over the entire back of the head.

10. Continue this action with the rest of the pieces that are hanging from the back buns. The final look will resemble a Celtic knot of hair.

11 and **12.** The hair from the top of the head is sectioned into 3 sections. The middle section is only about 1 1/2" thick. Referring back to page 36, form one side of the front of the hair into a victory roll that will rest above the eye and pin it in place with bobby pins.

13. Spread the back of the victory roll so that it rests flat against the head and pin it in place with bobby pins. Use the same actions for a victory roll on the left side so that there are 2 matching rolls. And note that the rolls do not need to be identical. There is room for asymmetry in this hairstyle.

14. Take the remaining last section of hair above the forehead and curl with a small curling iron.

15. Arrange the curls into a fluff on top of the head between the rolls and pin in place with small bobby pins. Hairspray for hold.

14

15

✦ The Scarf Roll ✦

Women came up with very interesting uses for scarves in the past. And for good reason. The onset of war and the fluctuation of women into the workforce called for some creative ways to get the hair up and away from machinery. The scarf for this look needs to be at least 30 inches long tip-to-tip. This ensures that it can reach around the head and tie. A basic bandana, when folded in half into a triangle and rolled thin will also be long enough to tie. A ribbon can be used to create a bow on top.

What you will need: hot rollers and clips, thermal spray, rattail comb, styling comb of choice, hairspray, pomade, bobby pins, ponytail holder, duckbill clips, ribbon or scarf

1. Set the hair in a basic roller set with hot rollers.

2. Section the hair into 2 sections between the front of the head and the back.

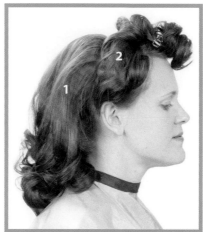

3. Take the back section of hair and tie it into a tight ponytail that rests at the bottom of the hairline at the nape of the neck.

4. Slide the ponytail holder down the section of hair so that it is only now holding the ends of the hair together.

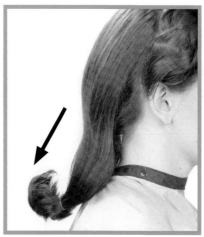

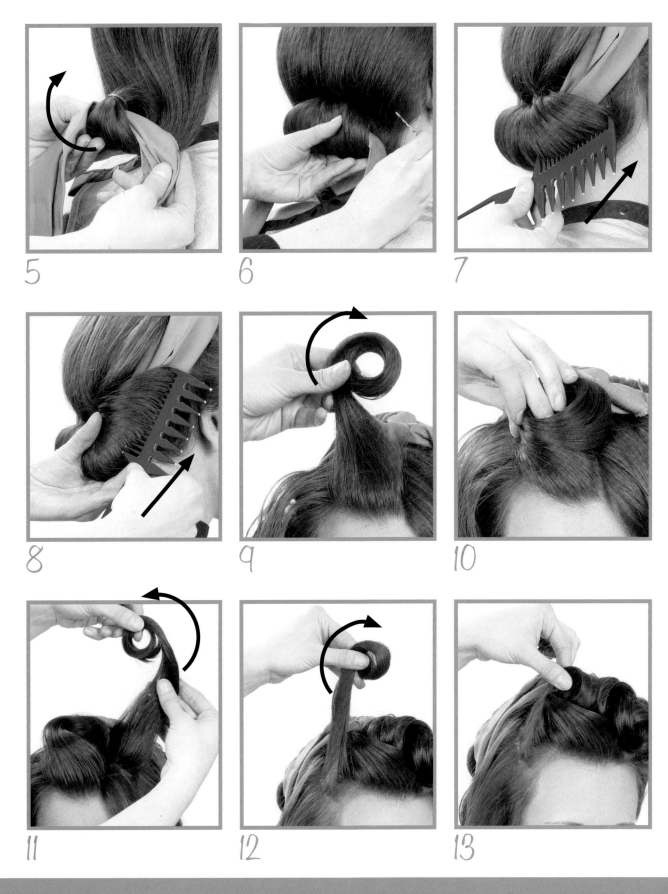

5. Place the middle of the scarf on the hair above the hair tie. Roll the ends of the hair up and over the scarf until the ends are tucked in between the hair and the scarf.

6. Continue rolling up until the roll has reached the nape of the neck and cannot roll anymore. Pin roll to hair on scalp with bobby pins.

7. Use a styling comb and insert the teeth into the roll.

8. Shift the ends of the roll up until the outer part of the roll is resting against the head and pin in place with bobby pins. Repeat on other side of roll.

9. Move to the front section of hair. The idea here is to create a pile of dry pin curls on top of the head. There is no specific pattern to use. Use small sections of hair.

10. Pull sections up and allow them to roll and sit on top of the head. Pin them in place with bobby pins.

11, 12, and **13.** Continue this until all the remaining pieces of hair are pinned up. Hairspray for hold.

✦ Veda ✦

This continuous roll in the back goes around the entire head and it may be helpful to wrap it in a hair net to keep it from coming apart over time. The style requires some length to the hair, but a small version is possible with shoulder length hair. It is modeled after the spoiled daughter of Joan Crawford in the Academy Award winning movie *Mildred Pierce.*

What you will need: large and small hot rollers and clips, thermal spray, rattail comb, styling brush, styling comb of choice, bobby pins, pomade, hairspray

1

2

1. The model's long bangs are set in small hot rollers that are rolled forward on-base. See page 22 for more information on hot rollers.

2. The rest of the hair is set in large hot rollers on-base rolling back and down toward the nape of the neck.

3 and **4.** After the rollers have cooled, remove the large rollers, but leave the small ones up front. Brush the hair back and down. Do not worry about maintaining curl. A trick to help hold the hair in place while rolling and keep the crown hair flat against the head is to use temporary bobby pins. Use your hands to pull the hair down at the nape of the neck and insert bobby pins toward the middle. Leave the side sections out for rolling.

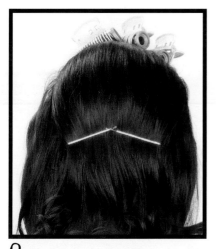

3

4

5

6

7

8

9

10

11

12

13

5. Using victory roll techniques, roll the side section away from the ear and back. Teasing the hair is very helpful for this style. It creates stability. You can also use a rat filler to create stability in the rolls. See page 38 for more information on creating victory rolls and page 41 for more information on rat fillers.

6. Spread the edges using your fingers in a scissor form to keep the roll smooth. Hairspray for hold.

7. Repeat steps 5 and 6 on the other side.

8. The middle section is left that was pinned flat against the back of the head. Remove the temporary bobby pins.

9 and **10.** Roll the hair up away from the neck in one last victory roll shape and pin in place.

11 and **12.** There will still be a gap between the rolls at this point. To connect them, gently take hold of some of the hair from one roll end and pull it toward the next roll. Pin and hairspray in place.

13. Remove the small hot rollers from the front of the style. Comb and tease the hair section up a little.

14. Let the hair fall forward and arrange the curls as desired. Hairspray for hold.

14

15

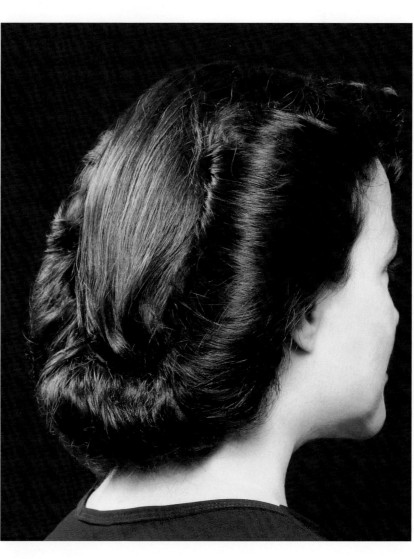

✦ French Twist ✦

French twists are used in a number of hairstyles in this book. Here is a basic tutorial on creating a French twist. This is a quick and easy way to get your hair up. If you set your hair in the front in pin curls first it is a wonderful retro style for dancing.

What you will need: medium hot rollers and clips, rattail comb, thermal spray, styling comb of choice, bobby pins, pomade, hairspray

1. Set hair in a basic hot roller set on-base. After the rollers have cooled, brush all the hair to one side.

2. Put a few bobby pins tightly against the hair down the center of where the twist will lie.

3. Then wrap the hair to the other side over the bobby pins.

4. Tuck the ends into the form.

5. Use many pins to pin in place. If you insert the pins where the roll meets the scalp horizontally, they will meet the pins underneath.

1

2

3

4

5

It is easy to create a fake bang when you do not want to commit to the cut. The elements of this style are influenced by a few things. The rounded fake bang mimics model Bettie Page's popular look. But this roll was also a style element used in the 1940s. The back of this hairstyle is inspired by a customer appearing in the 1946 movie, *The Best Years of Our Lives*.

What you will need: hot rollers and clips, small curling iron, thermal spray, rattail comb, pomade, hairspray, bobby pins, duckbill clips

1. Set the hair in a basic roller set with hot rollers.

2. Section the hair into 5 main sections. The back is split into 2 large sections. The front and top of the head are split into 3 small sections with the middle section being used for the bangs.

3 and **4.** Take the right side of the back section tightly in your hand and twist it towards the middle of the head into a French twist.

1

2

3

4

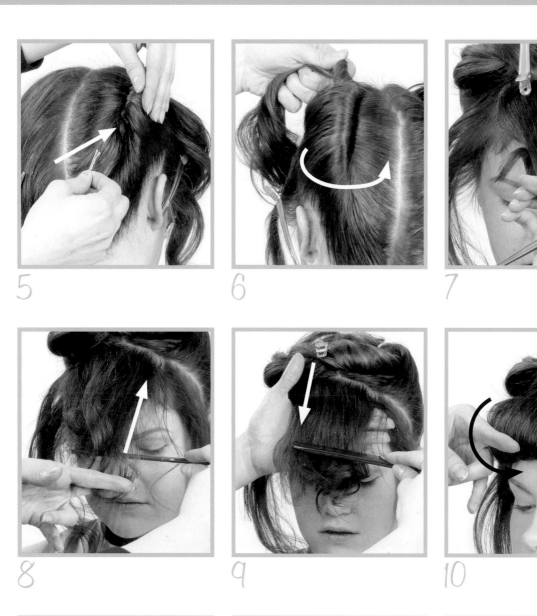

5

6

7

8

9

10

11

12

13

5. Pin the hair in place with bobby pins by inserting them into the indent where the twist sits on the scalp. This hides the pins.

6. Do the same actions on the left section of the back of the head.

7. There will still be ends left hanging out of the top of the French twists. Clip these out of the way until later. Take the middle section of hair from the top of the head.

8. Tease it to add fullness and lock to the shape that will be formed.

9. Smooth the hair on top with a comb and spray with hairspray to keep it smooth.

10. Roll the ends of the hair under toward the forehead and let the roll hang over the forehead. Use small bobby pins to pin this in place through the under sides of the roll.

11, 12, and **13.** Use a curling iron to curl the hair that is still sticking out of the top of the French twists and the hair that is still hanging from the sides behind the temples. Cross the curled hair over the top of the head and pin in place with bobby pins. Arrange the curls to create a curl fluff on top of the head.

14 and **15.** Take any remaining hair that is hanging down and pin with bobby pins toward the top of the head. Hairspray for hold.

✦ Red Hot ✦

This hairstyle is an alternative idea to victory rolls. Instead of letting the open end of the rolls show, the curls are left to cover and sit freely. The model has fine hair and someone with very thick hair may have a little trouble figuring out what to do with all the curls. If so, try replacing the front element with the front of another style like The Pompadour Twirl or The Scarf Roll.

What you will need: small curling iron, thermal spray, single prong clips, rattail comb, styling brush, styling comb of choice, bobby pins, hairspray, pomade, large barrette, duckbill clips

1

2

1. The hair is in 3 main sections. The natural part is left as the part for the hairstyle.

2. Begin curling the hair up toward the top of the head. Be sure to use thermal spray and a comb between the scalp and the iron for protection.

3. The left side is curled in the same manner with the hair rolling up toward the center of the head.

4. Curl the back in the same manner as the Pompadour Twirl on page 82. The lower curls are on-base curls and pinned in place to cool.

3

4

5

6

7

8

9

10

11

12

13

5. Continue to curl the back of the hair. As you work up, leave more of the base of the curl out of the curling iron so that the hair at the crown will remain straight.

6. Take the hair down in the back and brush into a ponytail.

7. Use a large barrette designed with a large opening to contain the entire back section of hair. The back of the head can be left alone at this point...

8, 9, and **10.** ...or continue with the style in the back by taking pieces of hair and pinning them up around the nape of the neck to create a curly chignon.

11 and **12.** Next, move to the front to the smaller section on the right side of the head. Pin pieces of hair up to the top of the head, allowing them to roll over much like a victory roll. But let the curly ends of the hair pieces sit outside of the roll.

13. Take the larger portion of hair on the right side of the head and tease it to create fullness and lock. Leave some strands out at the front hairline to add later.

14. Smooth the hair on the outside with a comb and rotate the hair in a twist to create a full roll.

15. Arrange remaining curls on top of the head and pin in place where needed. The finished style is more of a free form curl fluff with the ends unconnected. Hairspray for hold

14

15

✦ The Receptionist ✦

By the late 1950s, tighter curls relaxed and hair silhouettes grew. Perfection in waves gave way to simple curls with flexibility. Author and hairstylist Victor Vito in 1954 called his design for hairstyles that allowed for movement and energy *Mobiles*. The Receptionist style is inspired by the popular television show *Mad Men* and shows 2 options. If hair is not quite long enough for the ponytail look, dry pin curls are possible.

What you will need: hot rollers and clips, thermal spray, rattail comb, styling comb of choice, bobby pins, ponytail holder, hairspray, pomade

1

2

3

4

1. For this setting pattern, a small section of hair is left out at the front. For this model it is her bangs, but without bangs, a small section should still be left out. The hair is rolled in on-base large hot rollers that roll back and down. See page 22 for more information on hot rollers.

2. This hairstyle is made up in sections. The first section parted out is drawn with a line that goes from the top of one ear back across the bottom of the occipital bone to the top of the other ear. Clip the top hair out of your way. The lower section of hair is put in a French twist with the ends left out of the twist.

3. The next section is the hair from the top area that is behind the back of the ears. With this, a base for the bouffant will start. Tease the section and roll it into a victory roll and pin in place.

4. Create another section using hair in front of roll and tease for height. To create a lot of height in this style, it is best to start building the form at the bottom and work up, instead of working from the front to the back.

5

6

5. Lay the teased section over the victory roll. It will be hidden in the end. It was created purely for a base to pump up the height.

6. The sides are also teased to get width in the style.

7. Bring these side pieces and the top piece together in a ponytail.

8, 9, and **10.** There should still be some hair hanging at the front of the hair line. These side pieces will come across the back side of the hair to cover the ponytail holder. Insert bobby pins underneath to hide the ends of these last sections.

The final style has a couple options available. For a younger, daytime look, leave the 2 hanging pieces down. For a more sophisticated, evening look, take the hanging pieces and set dry pin curls.

7

8

9

10

✦ Golightly ✦

The look of Audrey Hepburn in *Breakfast at Tiffany's* is iconic. The most requested 1960s look is not hard to duplicate either. The simple elegance of her black dress and French-twisted hair will stand the test of time. This is a more complicated version of the style, but can be simplified for any skill level. To simplify it, separate the hair into fewer sections. The important part is to try to keep the height.

What you will need: hot rollers and clips, thermal spray, rattail comb, styling brush, styling comb of choice, bobby pins, hairspray, pomade

1

2

1. The hot rollers are set rolling to the side on-base at the front. To avoid gaps in the hairline of the finished style, the rollers should be set at a slight diagonal. See page 22 for more information on hot rollers.

2. The rest of the hair is rolled in a basic roller set on-base.

3. This illustrates the sections for this style. These sections can be pared down to simplify the hairstyle.

4. The style begins with section number 2. Tease the section for stability. Direct the section to the left and then roll it to the right to create a large, dry pin curl that spans the width of the top of the head.

3

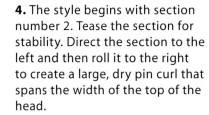

4

5. Pin the curl in place.

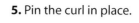

6. Working with section 3 the steps are the same as step 4 but working in the opposite direction. Tease the section for stability. Direct the section to the right and then roll it to the left to create a large, dry pin curl that spans the width of the top of the head.

7. The idea is that the 2 large, dry pin curls will stand on opposite sides of the head. A simpler option is to start with both of these sections as one and create one large curl to sit on top of the head.

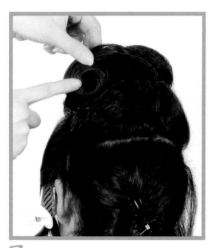

8 and **9.** Next working with section 4, create a French twist. See page 122 for more information on creating a French twist.

10. The last section is number 1 at the front of the head. Part the hair and bring the smaller section back around so that it lies between the top of the French twist and the dry pin curls. Pin and hairspray in place.

11. The final section is open to interpretation. It is very popular today for a front section like this to lie flat and swoop over the forehead. But in the movie, Hepburn's hair had lift in front. For that reason, that is how this hairstyle is done. Loosely hold the section in hand and gently bring around back.

12. Let the ends form a curl at the top of the French twist and pin in place. Hairspray in place.

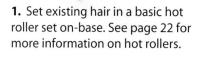

✦ Bouffant Bun ✦

This style was created using some synthetic hair and a hair looping tool. If working with very long hair, the added hair may not be necessary. But this also illustrates that with some creativity, shorter hair can do many things. The hair used was synthetic as it did not need to be curled, but the synthetic came with bent ends, which are important. The looping tool can be replaced with a tied ribbon. See directions for details.

What you will need: hot rollers and clips, thermal spray, rattail comb, styling comb of choice, bobby pins, ponytail holder, hairspray, pomade, synthetic hair for braiding, loop tool

1

2

1. Set existing hair in a basic hot roller set on-base. See page 22 for more information on hot rollers.

2. After the rollers have cooled, remove them and put existing hair in a tight and high ponytail. The higher the ponytail is the higher the style will sit on the head.

3. These directions use synthetic hair made for braiding to add fullness to the style. It is very long and is not attached to a weft.

4. Thread the synthetic hair through the ponytail holder.

3

4

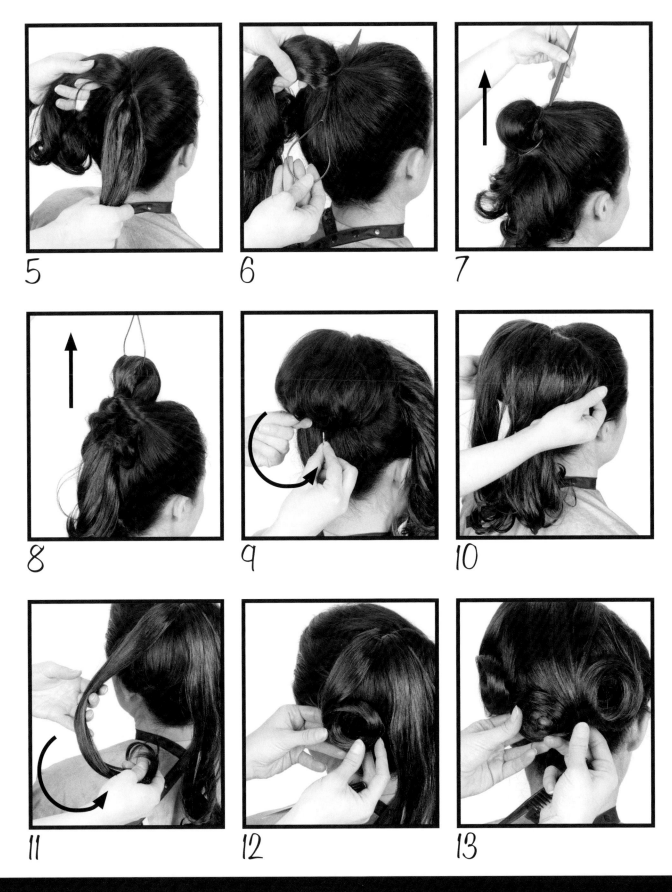

5. Equal amounts of the synthetic hair piece should hang on both sides of the ponytail holder.

6. Here, a looping hair tool is used, but a ribbon can substitute. Tie one end of the ribbon around the ponytail. Tuck the other end of the ribbon under the ponytail the same way the point of the looping tool is shown in image 6. Then pull the ponytail through in the same manner as image 7 and 8.

7 and **8.** The ponytail looping tool is threaded up underneath the ponytail. The ponytail is then threaded through the loop of the tool. Continue to pull the tool, or ribbon, so the hair comes all the way up and out of the top above the ponytail holder.

9. Put the synthetic hair off to the side. The existing hair will create the base of the style. Tease the hair, smooth over the top, and pin the ends underneath to create a bun.

10. Now take the synthetic hair and spread it over the top of the bun. Use hairspray and gently tease to control the hair and keep it spread over the real hair bun.

11, 12, and **13.** The final pieces are separated into 3 sections, or as many sections as desired. Bring each piece up to the bottom of the style and set dry pin curls. Pin and hairspray in place.

14 and **15.** This style is used to illustrate the use of braids as an accent or accessory. A similar strip of braiding hair was used here. It is tied off at each end with ponytail holders and then wrapped around the bun. Try this as a headband also.

14

15

✦ Beehive ✦

The beehive emerged in the late 1950s and stayed popular through the early 1960s. The name is descriptive of its resemblance to a bee's home that swirls around and tapers. It was also referred to as a B-52 because it resembled the nose of the WWII bomber.

What you will need: hot rollers and clips, thermal spray, rattail comb, styling comb of choice, bobby pins, hairspray, pomade

1

2

3

4

1. The hot rollers are set rolling sideways on-base at the front. To avoid gaps in the hairline of the finished style, the rollers should be set at a slight diagonal. See page 22 for more information on hot rollers.

2 and **3.** This hairstyle is made up in sections. The first section parted out is drawn with a line that goes from the top of one ear back across the bottom of the occipital bone to the top of the other ear. Clip the top hair out of your way. The lower section of hair is put in a French twist with the ends left out of the twist.

4. Let down the rest of the hair. Take a 2" by 2" section out of top of the crown and put it in a ponytail.

5. Wrap the ponytail around its base in a cone shape and pin and hairspray in place. Tease this section as needed to get volume in the cone shape.

6. The piece hanging from the top of the French twist is the first piece to wrap. Tease the hair section to add volume.

7. Teasing is a very important part of this style. It creates stability and volume. For even more stability, tease in a motion that goes in the direction that the hair will wrap. If the hair will wrap clockwise around the base, direct the hair clockwise and tease at the same time.

8. Continue wrapping sections both clockwise and counterclockwise around the base. Decide on direction based on which side of the style needs more hair at any given step.

9. A trick is to hide the ends of a section behind the section itself by tucking them in before pinning.

10. Continue wrapping hair and hairspraying.

11. Another helpful trick is to wrap with the ends of the hair still in the comb and hairspray while you work. The ends will lie more even.

12. Pinning should be done on the inner sections, but careful placement can be done on the finished style also.

13. If there are no bangs to work with, pull the last front sections above the forehead down and tight to swoop over the forehead and pin in place in the back. Hairspray for hold.

✦ Film Noir ✦

Hairstyles of the 1940s often involved curls which made the hair appear shorter. Actress Veronica Lake changed that trend with her long style. Her ends were curled, but the body of her hair was worn more straight. She was asked to change her style when young women wore their hair long to the factories and risked getting it caught in the machinery. This hairstyle is a great choice for anyone who wants to keep the appearance of long hair.

What you will need: water, shaping lotion, small velcro rollers, soft rollers, rattail comb, hooded hair dryer (optional), thin brush, styling comb of choice, bobby pins, hairspray, pomade

1

2

1. Begin by prepping the hair for a wet set as described on page 12. Part the hair above the outer corner of the eye and begin setting small velcro rollers. The partings should be on a diagonal to avoid gaps. Only 4 rollers are needed.

2. Set the rest of the hair using soft rollers. Keep the crown sections rolled off-base. And because the hair can take longer to dry in these rollers, try to keep the sections small. See page 24 for more information on soft rollers.

3. After the hair is dry, remove the velcro rollers and comb through the section with pomade on hands in an up motion. The pomade will help form and control frizz.

4. Gently allow the hair to fall to the side using fingers to spread wave. If using shorter hair, more combing will be required to get hair to lie in its wave. See page 46 for more information on combing waves. Remove soft rollers and brush bottom part of style. Use bobby pins to help hold peek-a-boo bang where desired.

3

4

✦ Bettie Bangs #1 ✦

Bettie Page's hairstyle of short cropped bangs is a wonderful retro look. For the girl who wants the bangs, but also wants to try something different with them, here is an option. Because, over time, hair at the hairline becomes trained to lie flat, part of this style is done as a wet set for staying power.

What you will need: water, shaping lotion, small velcro rollers, double prong clips, hot rollers and clips, thermal spray, rattail comb, hooded hair dryer (optional), styling comb of choice, hair combs, pomade, hairspray

1

2

1. Begin by prepping the bangs for a wet set as described on page 12. The 2 sections of this hairstyle consist of the Bettie Page bangs and the rest of the hair. The rest of the hair is left dry. The bangs are set with diagonal partings to avoid gaps in the finished style.

2. Roll the bangs to the side with velcro rollers on base. One roller on the outside is rolled away from the rest to create a separate curl later. Because the length of these bangs is very short, a wet set with velcro rollers offers the greatest control and curl. Double prong clips help to hold the rollers tight. See page 26 for more information on velcro rollers.

3. Set the dry hair in large hot rollers rolling down toward the neck. The side rollers turn slightly in toward the face. Note that these rollers are off-base rollers. Volume is not the goal with this style.

4. After the bangs have dried completely, with air or the hood dryer, remove the velcro rollers and comb the hair up and to the side. Use pomade and hairspray to hold height .

3

4

5

6

5. Form the ends into a high spit curl above the forehead with pomade.

6. Remove the hot rollers and comb the rest of the style down toward the floor to enhance the flat crown.

7. Pull the hair above the ears back 2".

8 and **9.** Use hair combs, barrettes, or bobby pins to hold back the sides. To insert hair combs, start the teeth 2" back from the hairline with the teeth pointing forward. Press the teeth into the hair closest to the scalp underneath to lock in place.

10. Finish the style by going around the perimeter and combing the hair under or toward the face. It is similar in look to the page boy, but the hair is not pinned underneath.

7

8

9

10

✦ Bettie Bangs #2 ✦

Bettie Page's hairstyle of short cropped bangs is a wonderful retro look. For the girl who wants the bangs, but also wants to try something different with them, here is another option in addition to the previous style. Because, over time, hair at the hairline becomes trained to lie flat, part of this style is done as a wet set for staying power.

What you will need: water, shaping lotion, small velcro rollers, double prong clips, hot rollers and clips, thermal spray, rattail comb, hooded hair dryer (optional), styling comb of choice, bobby pins, pomade, hairspray

1. Begin by prepping the bangs for a wet set as described on page 12. The 2 sections of this hairstyle consist of the Bettie Page bangs and the rest of the hair. The rest of the hair is left dry. Working with the wet set prepped bangs, part the hair horizontally.

2. Roll the bangs backward with velcro rollers on base. Because the length of these bangs is very short, wet set with velcro rollers offers the greatest control and curl. Double prong clips help to hold the rollers tight. See page 26 for more information on velcro rollers.

3. Set the bangs all in velcro rollers on-base rolling away from the face.

4. Set the rest of the hair in a basic on-base hot roller set with the hair rolling down toward the neck. See page 22 for more information on hot rollers.

1

2

3

4

5. Remove the hot rollers after they have cooled and brush the hair back and out of the way. Use pomade on hands to distribute through the hair and to control.

6. After the bangs have dried completely, with air or the hood dryer, comb them straight up.

7. Tease the bangs to add fullness and stability.

8. Smooth the bangs back into a small pompadour. Hairspray in place.

9. Set the rest of the style in large, dry pin curls and victory rolls directly on top of the head.

10. Roll the hair in various directions to create piles of curls.

11. Continue to pile curls on the head and pin in place.

12. Finish the style with all the curls directly on top of the head. Hairspray for hold.

11

12

✦ The Silent Film Star ✦

In the 1920s and early 1930s, girls cut their hair short in a "bob" and wore finger waves. This version gives the feeling of finger waves, but with more volume. Do not pull the hair away from the scalp. Keep the roots against the scalp and the style will stay a little more flat. If hair is longer, try pinning it up to give the feeling of a bob. Also play with the combing of the style. By letting the bottom curls fluff out and combing hair above the forehead back, a style similar to Jean Harlow's can be achieved.

What you will need: water, shaping lotion, hairpins, small velcro rollers, rattail comb, hooded hair dryer (optional), thin brush, styling comb of choice, duckbill clips, bobby pins, pomade, hairspray

1

2

1. Begin by prepping the hair for a wet set as described on page 12. Part the hair above the outer corner of the eye and begin setting in medium pin curls. Refer to page 27 for instructions on pin curls.

2. The rows of pin curls alternate in direction. The first row on the top of the head is set in reverse counterclockwise curls. The row directly below it is set in forward clockwise curls.

3. After the top has been set, move down to the sides and back. Set these in consecutive rows that go all the way around the head. Imagine that the wave of hair needs to be consistent all the way around so the curls must be consistent. The first row on the right side is a reverse counterclockwise pin curl. The row below is forward clockwise curls and the third again reverse counterclockwise.

4. On the left side of the head, the curls are set the same, but seem different because of the relation to the face. The first row is still counterclockwise, but in relation to the left side of the face, it is a forward roll. If there are hairs that are too short to pin curl, use small velcro rollers instead.

3

4

5

6

5. After the hair is dry, begin releasing the curls. For this style, the curls are not allowed to fall out away from the head because the style is suppose to lay more flat. Instead push them in toward the scalp before pulling down. See page 34 for more details on pulling out a curl.

6. For the curls that go around the back of the head, there will be a ridge wave along only the top. Comb it into its wave shape as described on page 46.

7. After forming the ridge, use pomade and hairspray to separate curls to create a controlled curl fluff around the neck.

8. Comb the top above the forehead into a wave and connect it to the lower curls. Use the duckbill clip and hairspray to help form the wave.

9. Use bobby pins hidden inside the style to hold hair in its form.

10. Play with pomade around the face to form some of the curls into spit curls that lie against the face. Women used egg whites to stick spit curls to their face, but a strong-hold gel can be used for a more sanitary option. See page 45 for information on spit curls.

7

8

9

10

Cascading Curls

This is another great, long-lasting style for someone with fine hair that does not hold a curl for long. The wet set can be slept on, brushed out, and restyled without too much relaxing. The bangs of this set also add an extra pompadour height to the front.

What you will need: water, shaping lotion, hairpins, double prong clips, rattail comb, hooded hair dryer (optional), styling comb of choice, pomade, hairspray

1

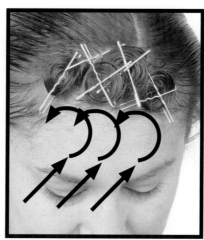

2

1. Begin by prepping the hair for a wet set as described on page 12. The model's hair is cut in very long layers and has a thin section of long bangs. Separate out the bangs. Refer to page 27 for instructions on pin curls.

2. Set the bangs in small pin curls. The direction the hair is pulled will be the opposite of the direction it will lay. By doing this, the maximum volume is achieved above the forehead. The bangs of this style will be brushed over to the right side of the face, so for volume, start the curls by pulling the hair back towards the left side of the head.

3 and **4.** Set the rest of the hair in alternating rows of large pin curls. Set them off-base and use double prong clips to hold them in place.

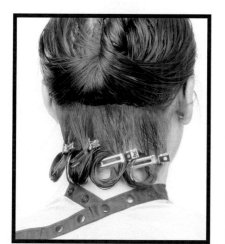

3

4

5

6

5 and **6.** Because the curls will be allowed to fall freely, they do not need to line up perfectly. It is only important to keep the size consistent.

7. After the hair is dry, start taking the back pin curls down one row at a time starting from the bottom.

8. As sections are taken down, comb hair and use pomade on fingers to control fly-aways and direction of waves.

9. Use pomade on the ends of hair to smooth and shine.

10. The last layer of large pin curls can be brushed together and formed into waves. See page 46 for more on waves from pin curls.

7

8

9

10

11

12

13

11, 12, and **13.** Release the small pin curls set into the bangs. Use a styling comb to comb up and then over to the right side of the face. Comb bangs into a pin curl wave. Be sure to practice wave techniques for a better understanding.

14. The finished style has volume all around and height at the forehead. Hairspray for hold.

14

✦ The Contessa ✦

Curling short hair can be tricky. For this style, small velcro rollers can be substituted if the hair is just too short to wrap into a pin curl. This style also lends itself well to a curling iron. It does not require complete uniformity. Just keep the crown of the head straight so the hairstyle is sophisticated. This look is inspired by actress Ava Gardner in *The Barefoot Contessa*.

What you will need: water, shaping lotion, single prong clips, rattail comb, hooded hair dryer (optional), pomade, hairspray

1

2

1. Begin by prepping the hair for a wet set as described on page 12. Part the hair above the outer corner of the eye and set the hair in stand-up pin curls. Refer to page 27 for instructions on pin curls.

2. These pin curls, although consistent in size and general direction, can be a little more free-form.

3. Roll all the curls down toward the floor. Keep them around the hairline to form a halo effect. Leave the crown straight.

4. After the hair is dry, with pomade on your fingers, finger through the hair and arrange the curl as desired. Hairspray for hold.

3

4

✦ Bang Wave ✦

Waves at the hairline can flow in many different directions. It is important, though, to roll the pin curls in the correct direction to fit properly. The basics of a wave from a pin curl are laid out in the Combing Out section of the book. Please refer to that section to practice the technique. Once the basic idea is understood the possibilities are endless. This wave is designed to wave at a diagonal creating a ridge at the hairline.

What you will need: water, shaping lotion, single prong clips, rattail comb, hooded hair dryer (optional), styling comb of choice, styling brush, bobby pins, pomade, hairspray, hair combs, duckbill clips

1. Begin by prepping the hair for a wet set as described on page 12. This hairstyle has 2 main sections. The top section will be formed into waves parted down the center and moving back and out. The rest of the hair will be shaped into a curl fluff. Refer to pages 27 for instructions on pin curls.

2. Part the hair down the center. Part out the section for the first stand-up pin curl with a triangle base. All of these curls will be set with triangle bases to avoid gaps in the finished style.

3. To the right of the part, 2 rows of stand-up pin curls are set for volume. The front row is 3 curls and the back is 2 curls. They roll out clockwise away from the part.

4. The exact opposite of counterclockwise stand-up pin curls are set on the opposite side of the part.

1

2

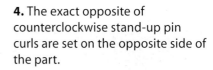

3

4

5

6

7

8

9

10

11

12

13

5. Set the rest of the hair in small velcro rollers. The option of setting the rest of the hair in pin curls for authenticity is there, but for time purposes velcro or soft rollers work well also. Set the rollers off-base to avoid volume. A flat crown is desired here. See page 26 for more information on velcro rollers.

6, 7, and **8.** After the hair has dried completely, with air or the hood dryer, remove the rollers, but leave the pin curls for now. Brush out hair and pin sides of hair back with hair combs, barrettes, or bobby pins. To insert hair combs, start the teeth 2″ back from the hairline with the teeth pointing forward. Press the teeth into the hair closest to the scalp underneath to lock in place.

9. Remove the single prong clips from both sides. Work with one side at a time. Pin the side not being worked with out of the way to avoid snagging. Begin by combing hair back and to the side slightly away from the part.

10. Comb this section of hair into a wave. See page 46 for more information on combing waves from pin curls.

11. To deepen the wave after forming, try inserting the teeth of the comb behind it and pressing the wave forward.

12. Arrange the rest of the section of hair as desired in dry pin curls or continue to wave the hair back.

13. Use bobby pins to help hold the hair section in its place. Repeat steps on other side. Hairspray for hold.

✦ Hat Hair ✦

Hats were an important accessory. The styles, shapes, and colors of vintage hats are endless and they can be found easily at antique stores and vintage clothing shops. But putting a hat over curls would wreak havoc on the style and make the hat sit too high. This style is designed to leave a nice nook for the hat to sit in. Many of the styles shown have a straight crown area to accommodate hats.

What you will need: water, shaping lotion, hairpins, rattail comb, velcro rollers, hooded hair dryer (optional), styling brush, thin brush, bobby pins, ponytail holder, hairspray, pomade, duckbill clips

1

2

3

4

1. Begin by prepping the hair for a wet set as described on page 12. Part hair into 4 main sections. The front above the eyes is centered and 3" wide by 2" deep. The 2 diagonal sections on the side of the head go down to the ears and are 2" deep. Refer to page 27 for instructions on pin curls.

2. Over-direct the first pin curl upwards before rolling into a reverse counterclockwise curl to achieve the round arch on top of the finished style.

3. Set the next row opposite for a skip wave of forward clockwise curls, but set these so that they point down.

4. Set the last row in reverse counterclockwise pin curls to finish the wave. The important thing to remember is that with this style, the wave will be at a diagonal, so the pin curls need to be set on a diagonal and slightly skew the pivot point so the finished curl will "point" in the right direction. Repeat the steps on the left side of the head by reversing the clockwise direction of the curl. The top and bottom rows are clockwise and the middle row is counterclockwise.

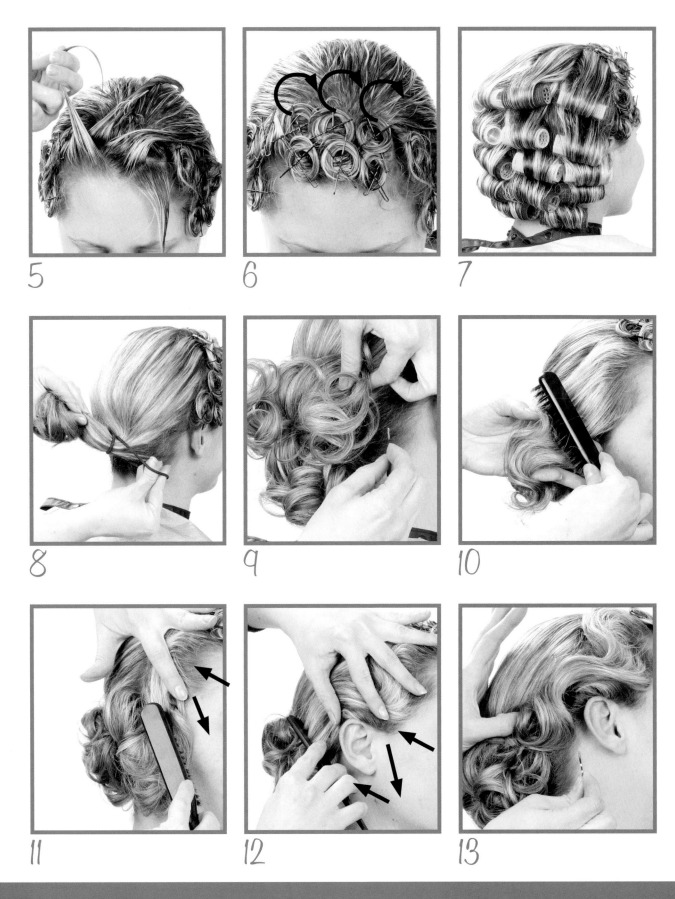

5 and **6.** Set the top section into clockwise pin curls, but to achieve height, over direct to the left. After drying, it will be brushed out to the right.

7. Set the hair in back in off-base velcro rollers. Let the hair air dry or dry completely under a hooded hair dryer.

8. After hair is dry, remove velcro roller and brush curls. Tie hair into a ponytail.

9. With pomade on fingers, separate curls and arrange and pin to create a curly bun at the nape of the neck.

10, 11, and **12.** Follow the directions laid out on pages 42-47 to form the sides of the style into a wave.

13. Keep the wave close to the head and connect it to the element on the back. Pin with bobby pins.

14 and **15.** Comb the bangs up and over to the left side of the head and arrange the curly ends as desired. Hairspray for hold.

14

15

✦ Asymmetric Style ✦

Vintage hairstyles do not need to be equally proportioned on both sides of the head. It was very common for there to be more volume on certain areas of a style to balance out the face or draw attention away from another area. Actress Jane Russell often wore her hair with more curls on one side of her head than the other.

What you will need: water, shaping lotion, single prong clips, sponge rollers and end wraps, rattail comb, hooded hair dryer (optional), styling comb of choice, pocket brush, bobby pins, barrettes, hairspray, pomade, duckbill clips

1. Begin by prepping the hair for a wet set as described on page 12. The hair is separated into 2 main sections. The top section is roughly 3" x 3" square and centered.

2 and **3.** Set the top section into stand-up pin curls that roll clockwise to the left side of the head. They should point forward at a slight diagonal. Refer to page 27 for instructions on pin curls.

4. To avoid gaps at the hairline in front and on the sides, section at diagonals before rolling the hair.

5

6

7

8

9

10

11

12

13

5. Set the rest of the hair in small sponge rollers or velcro rollers so that they roll down toward the floor. Let air dry or dry under a hooded hair dryer.

6. When dry, start unrolling the hair from the rollers starting at the bottom and working your way up. Use hairspray and pomade to help control fly-aways and smooth.

7. Comb the curls with a large-tooth styling comb to create a curl fluff.

8. Smooth the sides down and clip down with barrettes so that the curls fluff low around the ears.

9. Release the pin curls from the top section and brush out.

10, 11, and **12.** Using pomade on your fingers, separate the curls and arrange so that they come forward and to the left side. The curls should bunch up around each other on the side of the forehead.

13. Use bobby pins to secure the style and finalize the silhouette. Hairspray for hold.

Other Options

Decorating hair with adornments is a tradition as old as brushing it. Hair picks made from precious metals have been found in the tombs of ancient Egypt. Ancient Greek women tied their hair up with bands, ribbons, and strings of pearls. Geishas are famous for the elaborate flowers and combs they wear.

When dressing for polite society, women in the early 20th century had to think about much more than their neatly-pressed dresses and gloves. The look was not complete without some type of decoration in the hair. In this section there are some basic and popular options from the 1920s -1960s.

To the left, you will see a cap made of only netting and flowers. Net veils over the face were not just for weddings and funerals; they were appropriate for all formal occasions. Notice in photographs of the time period what sort of hair accessories women were wearing and whether it was for pure decoration or a more utilitarian purpose.

Accessories

A hair accessory is the perfect way to finish a look. They were very popular for many reasons. If a woman had the same hairstyle for 5 days because she didn't want to wash it out and do it all over again, changing accessories changed everything.

Ribbons were a popular option to dress up a hairstyle in the 1930s. In the 1940s, the Pacific received a lot of attention, including the island flowers. In the 1950s scarves were a popular hair accessory.

Decoration is only half of it. They also serve a utilitarian purpose, holding hair in different areas. Barrettes and hair combs hold the hair in place and can easily be decorated with bows or flowers. Scarves are a fashionable way to protect hair from the elements or to get it out of the way.

They also solve problems. If there is a transition between elements in a hairstyle, an accessory can enhance it. If you have messed something up and the transition does not seem to work, an accessory can camouflage it. If you are just having a bad hair day and don't love the way it looks in the mirror, an accessory can cover it.

Whatever the purpose, there is no better way to authenticate a vintage look. In Resources in the back of the book, there is a list of online retailers. Use the accessories on these web pages as inspiration for what you can do.

Snood

The Snood has been a decorative but practical hair accessory for centuries. Their highest popularity in the twentieth century was in the early 1940s. They were a stylish way to keep your long hair out of factory machinery.

Hats

Hairstyles in the early and mid-twentieth century were accommodating to hats. Hats were an important and common accessory. The flat crown techniques on many styles in the book are designed to work with hats.

Feathers

Feathers are used more for an evening hair accessory to be worn with a dress. They were most popular in the 1920s with flappers.

Headband

Headbands are most associated with the 1950s and 1960s.

Hair Combs

Hair combs have been used for decoration and hair fastening by many over the centuries. In ancient Japan, Geisha adorned their hair with them. Victorians decorated them with jewels or glass for a more affordable alternative.

Barrettes

Barrettes can be decorated many ways. And they are useful in fastening your hair back.

Bows

Ribbons serve well as decoration and utilitarian purposes. Tie one in a bow to hold back your hair or to close the end of a braid.

Ribbon

Scarves

Scarves have so many options. Tie it around a ponytail for the 1950s or tie one in a bow on top of your head for the 1940s.

Flowers

The type of flower in your hair says a lot about the personality and style of the wearer.

Multiples of the same flowers in a line around a style adds emphasis and motion.

This unique type of flower was created so the petals would lie against the scalp. The petals are large enough that with conforming to the head the flower looks almost like a small hat. Flower designed and created by Rockabilly Rootz, www.myspace.com/rockabillyrootz.

✦ Flower ✦

There are a number of resources for purchasing flowers attached to hair fasteners. Online, local boutiques, and accessory stores often have a variety (see resources section). But sometimes the right color for the right outfit is hard to find.

At the local craft store, all the ingredients needed for the perfect flower are available.

What you will need: fabric flower of choice, a hair fastener like a barrette or large bobby pin, felt, wire cutters, hot glue gun

1 and **2.** Use the wire cutters to cut the flower off of its stem. Fake flowers often have a wire inside the stem for shaping. Be careful not to cut too close or the flower may fall apart.

3. Slip a small piece of felt between the prongs of the bobby pin or barrette.

4 and **5.** Spread a small amount of glue from the hot glue gun on to the felt.

6. Glue felt to flower and hold in place for a few seconds. One prong of the hair fastener will be glued in between the felt and the flower.

1

2

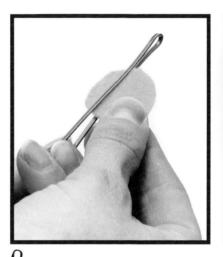

3

4

5

6

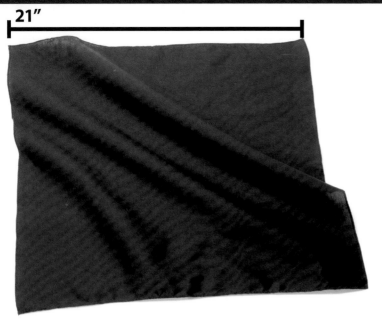

21"

1

5"

2

3

The Rosie/Protect your Style

Women came up with some creative ways to protect their hair. It took a lot of time and effort, so protecting it while sleeping or while working in a factory where sparks were flying was important. This seemingly everyday solution became the symbol of a woman's powerful role during the war.

When America entered the war, corporations needed to fill a huge gap in the labor force. The male work force was dwindling as men joined the armed forces. The solution was to fill factory positions with women. But women did not initially jump at the opportunity to work producing war equipment. So the government launched a propaganda campaign that included a fictional character "Rosie the Riveter". She symbolized how women at home could serve the boys overseas and their country.

This look can be slept on to help protect pin curls if allowing them to dry overnight. If you have an existing style for a few days, pinning the hair loosely back up in the curls and wrapping will help it last through sleep. Or pile some dry curls on top of the head for a look to wear all day.

4

5

Bandanas can be found in most craft and hobby stores and come in a wide variety of colors. Their basic size is 21" by 21" square. The diagonal of the bandana comes out to 30" tip to tip. Here are directions for both a headband look and a turban look.

1 and **2.** For a headband, fold in half and then fold into thirds. The bandana is now roughly 5" wide.

3. It will wrap easiest around the head if the longest side of the folded bandana is at the bottom when it is wrapped around the head.

4. Tie in place in a double knot.

5. For a turban style, only fold the bandana in half. Wrap around so the folded side is at the bottom and tie the front corners together.

6 . Fold down the sides almost like wrapping a gift.

7. Bring the final point down and tuck under the knot to hold in place.

6

7

✦ Finishing Touches ✦

Many of the cosmetic companies we know today began in the early part of the 20th century. A chemist named Thomas Williams created the first commercial mascara. He blended Vaseline and coal dust, first for his sister Mabel, and then marketed it as Maybelline (Mabel and Vaseline). A Polish immigrant named Max Faktor began as a makeup artist and wig-maker, and may have been the one to coin the term "make-up". After he arrived in Los Angeles, he changed the spelling to Factor and developed cosmetics for use in films. His clients included Jean Harlow, Bette Davis, and Claudette Colbert. Drawing on his experience with actresses such as Marilyn Monroe on the set of *Gentlemen Prefer Blondes*, Ben Nye developed cosmetics specially designed for film and theater.

Beauty makeup has not changed significantly over the years. Today's beauty books can show you techniques that will fit well with vintage hairstyles. But there were some identifiable trends in the mid-20th century; these included heavier liner and lashes on the top eyelid than on the bottom and well-defined lips, no matter what shade of rose. If you really want a "complete" vintage look, this section will show you steps to get it.

Eyebrows

Movies stars had the biggest influence on how women wore their eyebrows. In a silent film, actors did not have the inflection in the voice to convey emotion, so they relied on facial expression. Makeup artists in the 1920s used heavy lines and shading to contour the face so that every expression was intensified. Eyebrows softened as sound came in to play, but they still needed definition to show up well on black and white film.

Eyebrow shapes of actresses varied widely and could get very severe. But for a generally flattering shape for every facial type, follow your own bone structure.

1. Using a brush to measure, the inside end of the brow at the bridge of the nose should line up between the outer nostril and inside corner of the eye.

1

2

3

4

5

2. It should then graduate upward with the highest point lining up with the outside point of the iris.

3. The outer corner of the eyebrow lines up on a diagonal with the outer corner of the eye and the nostril.

4 and **5.** Using either a brow shadow and an angled brush or an eyebrow pencil, use small strokes that follow the hair growth and work your way out from the inner end to outer tip of the eyebrow. The color of the product used should generally be in the same tonal range as the color of the hair on top of the head.

Winged Eyeliner

It is hard to say there are any certain eyeliner styles which are synonymous with the early- and mid-twentieth century. Eyeliner, like eyebrows, was an important part of movie makeup to convey emotion in facial expression and accentuate the eyes on black and white film. Early eyeliner was actually a kohl product used to darken around the eyes. Later, pencils and liquids became available. The winged eyeliner style was an important fad beginning in the 1950s. It can be done with a liquid liner or a high quality well-sharpened eyeliner pencil.

This demonstration is done using a liquid liner and angled brush. Most liquid liners come with a brush that is usually attached to the cap, but a thin angled brush is easier to control and can make the thinnest of lines.

1

2

3

1 and **2.** Begin with the outside corner and decide how far out the point will go.

3. Work in toward the inner point of the eye. As the line continues in it gets thinner.

4 and **5.** Make sure the line continues to the inner point. If continuing the line on the lower lid, start on the outer corner again, but only work in 2/3 of the way.

4

5

⋆ Red Lips ⋆

"I didn't have my lipstick on yet!"

Marilyn Monroe
Bus Stop, 1956

The most important part of a red lip is the color chosen. More often than not, it will be better to use a red that has blue undertones. The best thing to do is go to a makeup counter where you can try it before you buy it. It never looks the same on the lips as it does in the tube.

1

2

3

4

5

6

1, 2, and **3.** Lining the lip is optional, but with a red lip there is little room for error. The liner is suggested to get the outer shape right and experiment with different vintage shapes.

4, 5, and **6.** Apply lipstick all over lips. Include the inner corners, otherwise when the mouth is opened, there will be an obvious break in the lip line.

7 and **8.** To avoid the dreaded red teeth, stick index finger in mouth, close lips over it, and pull out. This gets red off the inside of the lips. Finish with a gloss.

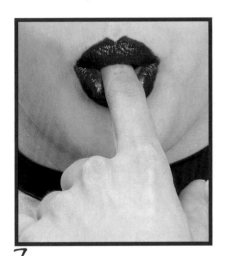

7

8

✦ Nails ✦

The coloring of fingernails in some form or another dates back to ancient China. But what we know today as nail polish came on to the market in the 1920s. The development of automobile paint is accredited with providing the technology of nail lacquer.

Nail shape and paint followed certain trends for most of the early and middle part of the twentieth century. It was considered feminine for nails to be long and past the tips of the fingers. The popular free edge shape changed over the years from a point to oval.

Paint styles fluctuated some, but the most common detail that perpetuated through the 1920s and on into the 1940s left the lanula of the nail clean. Although completely painting the entire nail a red or rose color was not uncommon. In the late 1920s, a product called Society Nail White became available. It was painted under the free edge and left to dry and gave the nail a healthy white color, thereby paving the way for the modern French manicure.

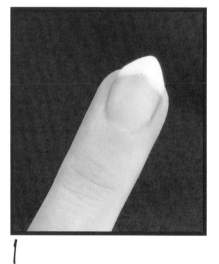

1

2

The bare moon manicure is the style most associated with a vintage look.

In all instances, the lunula of the nail is left bare while the rest of the nail is painted. The lunula is the half moon shaped white spot just in front of the cuticle at the base of the nail.

What you will need: Nail polish color of your choice and clear top coat, acetone, rounded flat art paintbrush, paper towel

3

4

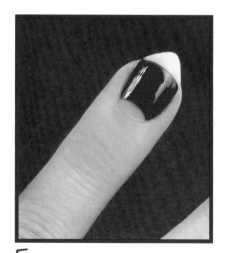

5

1930s Nail

1. The most unique nail shape of the 1930s was a pointed free edge.

2. Then paint the majority of the nail with polish. Leave the free edge and lanula bare.

3. Dip a small round paint brush in acetone and press it on a paper towel to get rid of excess liquid. Acetone is the best at dissolving red polish without smearing.

4. Use the brush to clean and finish the lines of the lanula and free edge.

5. This was a popular paint style worn by actresses including Bette Davis.

1940s Nail
Another possible choice worn in the 1940s is similar in concept, but with a more thin tip.

6. In the 1940s, an oval shaped free edge was considered most attractive.

7. Paint the nail leaving the lanula clean.

8. Use a brush with acetone like the 1930s nail to clean the edge of the bare moon.

9. Then use the brush to clean a very small strip of polish off of the free edge. This leaves an unpolished tip all the way around that is about 1/16 of an inch thick.

10. A 1940s oval nail can also be painted a more natural nail color.

1950s Nail
11. By the 1950s and into the 1960s, the simple and clean French Manicure was most popular.

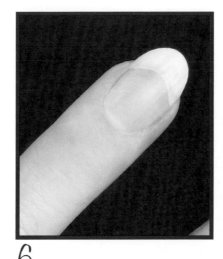

6

7

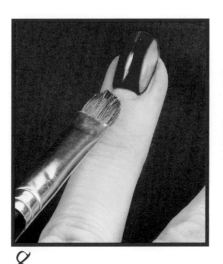

8

9

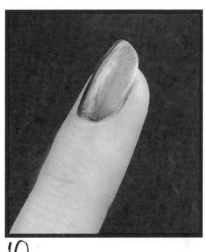

10

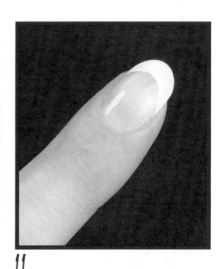

11

Resources

There are many resources available to find great hair tools, products, and accessories. These are just a few suggestions if you are not sure where to start. Neither HRST Books nor the author guarantee products from any of these sources.

Beauty Products and Tools
Sally Beauty Supply, www.sallybeauty.com for store locations
Folica Beauty Supply, www.folica.com to order
Your local drugstore or discount department store carries many of the products and tools in this book.

Pre-made Fabric Hair Flowers
Many sites carry pre-made flowers that are ready to be worn. These sites have a nice wide selection of styles.
www.littlebellesboutique.com
www.flowerclip.com
www.myspace.com/rockabillyrootz

Barrettes
JCrew clothing stores, www.jcrew.com for store locations, barrettes not carried online
www.eleganthairacc.com
www.mybabyjo.com, also carries flowers and bandanas

Snoods
www.reddressshoppe.com, also carries decorative hair combs
www.gentlemansemporium.com
www.dancestore.com

Bandanas and Ribbon
www.bandanaworld.com, has every color of bandana under the sun
Joann Fabric and Craft Stores, www.joann.com for store locations
Michaels, www.michaels.com for store locations

Scarves
www.thevintagescarf.com
www.coveryourhair.com, carries a cute assortment of hair accessories
Your local department store or thrift store will also have many scarves.

Hats
Hats are available on many vintage clothing store web sites, but one word of caution. Hats are like clothing. There are different sizes to fit different heads. Hats can easily be found in your local antique and vintage clothing stores and you can try it on to make sure it fits before you buy it.

Vintage Wedding Veils and Hats
www.vintagewedding.com
www.cherishedbride.com
www.dollsandlace.com
www.saragabriel.com, new veils inspired by vintage
www.headpiece.com, offers reproductions of vintage veils

Other
More information on historical hair and makeup at The Bobby Pin Blog, www.bobbypinblog.blogspot.com.

Bibliography

Books

Alpert, Arlene, et al. *Milady's Standard: Cosmetology*. New York: Thomson Learning, 2004.

Anderson, Ivan. *Creative Hairshaping and Hairstyling You Can Do*. Hollywood: Ivan Coiffure Studios, 1947.

Corson, Richard. *Fashions in Hair: The First Five Thousand Years*. London: Peter Owen, 1980.

Jones, Charles R., *Barber Shop History and Antiques*. Atglen: Schiffer Publishing Ltd., 1998.

Martignette, Charles G., and Louis K. Meisel. *The Great American Pin-Up*. Taschen, 2002.

Newberry, Louis. *Hairstyle Design*. Newberry Publishers, 1946.

Sherrow, Victoria. *Encyclopedia of Hair: A Cultural History*. Westport: Greenwood Press, 2006.

Turudich, Daniela. *1940s Hairstyles*. West Palm Beach: Streamline Press, 2001.

Vito, Victor. *Top Secrets of Hair Styling*. New York: Sudan Press, 1954.

DVDs

The Best of Film Noir. Writer Christopher Case. Commentator Jeffrey Wells. Passport International Entertainment, 1999.

Hollywood Biographies: The Leading Ladies. Passport Video. 2006. 5-Disc Series.

Websites

"Celebrity photos, movie star photos, sports pictures, and historical interest pictures." www.classicphotos.com

"A History of Nail Care." www.nailtechnician.co.nz/html/history_of_nail_care.html

"Maybelline - History." www.maybelline.co.uk/about_us/l282l283.htm

"Rosie the Riveter: Women Working During World War II." www.nps.gov/pwro/collection/website/rosie.htm

Image © Eric Weber www.eweber.com

About the author

Hair and makeup artist Lauren Rennells works in the photography and film industry. She freelances providing unique designs for advertisements, films, and television. Her passion for hairstyles of the past led her to write *Vintage Hairstyling: Retro Styles with Step-by-Step Techniques*. She also provides more information and techniques for historical hair and makeup on her blog at www.bobbypinblog.blogspot.com.

Order Information

To order more copies of *Vintage Hairstyling: Retro Styles with Step-by-Step Techniques*, go to www.vintagehairstyling.com for credit card orders or to find a retailer near you.

Or for check or money order, mail payment made to:
HRST Books
Attn: Vintage Hairstyling
P.O. Box 18429
Denver, Colorado
80218

Retail Cover Price: See back cover for price.
Sales Tax: Please add 7.72% for products shipped to Colorado addresses.
Shipping: Please include your shipping address with orders.
U.S.: $6.00 for first book, $3.00 for each additional book.
International: $13.00 US for first book, $6.00 US for each additional book.